LAWS OF TRADE

AN

ESSAY

ON THE

LAWS OF TRADE

IN REFERENCE TO THE

WORKS OF INTERNAL IMPROVEMENT

IN THE

UNITED STATES

BY

CHARLES ELLET JR.

[1839]

REPRINTS OF ECONOMIC CLASSICS

AUGUSTUS M. KELLEY · PUBLISHERS
NEW YORK · 1966

First Edition 1839
(Richmond: P. D. Bernard, 1839)

Reprinted 1966 by
Augustus M. Kelley · Publishers

Library of Congress Catalogue Card Number
65-26363

PRINTED IN THE UNITED STATES OF AMERICA
by SENTRY PRESS, NEW YORK, N. Y. 10019

AN ESSAY

ON

THE LAWS OF TRADE.

AN ESSAY

ON THE

LAWS OF TRADE,

IN REFERENCE TO THE

WORKS OF INTERNAL IMPROVEMENT

IN THE

UNITED STATES.

BY CHARLES ELLET, Jr.

CIVIL ENGINEER,

Chief Engineer of the James River and Kanawha Improvement.

RICHMOND:

PRINTED BY P. D. BERNARD.

1839.

LETTER

TO THE PRESIDENT AND DIRECTORS OF THE JAMES

RIVER AND KANAWHA IMPROVEMENT.

Gentlemen :

My relation to the company whose interests are under your direction, might be sufficient of itself to justify addressing to you a
communication on any subject connected with
the great design you are prosecuting.

Engaged, as you are, in the magnificent enterprise of opening a line of communication
from tide water to the western boundary of the
state, with a view to obtain possession of the
trade passing between a vast area of the country and the ocean, it is right to presume that
you are desirous of investigating its prospects,
and of knowing what are the points on which
its success is mainly dependent. And intrust-
ed as I have been, by your confidence, with the

professional charge of a work which will lead to the expenditure of many millions, it is proper that I should submit to you my opinions on the most important questions which are likely to require your consideration, and state fairly the principles that have governed me in deciding on the plans which I have deemed it expedient to recommend for your adoption.

At this period of your operations it is particularly apposite to ask your consideration of the subject before you.

You have now a line of 150 miles of canal on the point of being thrown open for navigation, and on which your attention is about to be occupied with the establishment of a tariff of toll. It is therefore important to know by what principle the charges for the use of your line should be regulated, so that it may be rendered most profitable to the stockholders, and most beneficial to the community. These charges are not optional with the board, but must be governed by certain fixed and palpable principles. They depend on the construction of the work, the length of the line, the proportions of water and land transportation, the nature of

the article, the ability and position of rivals,
the value of the commodity in the mart at
which you deliver it, and the mode and place
where the trade reaches the improvement.

The toll proper to be levied is a subject of
direct calculation, and I have endeavored to indicate for the object, a method by which all the
considerations that influence its value may at
once receive their proper weight, and the tariff
be such as to secure the greatest amount of
revenue to the company.

You have authorised me to extend the survey of your line from the western end of the
portion now in the course of construction to the
Ohio river. This duty is accomplished, and I
have recently reported on the result of the examination, and presented my views on the proper mode of continuing the improvement, and
the plan and location that should be adopted.

In directing these operations, and deciding on
the points at issue, I have frequently been governed by the views which I entertain on the
subject of the LAWS OF TRADE; and it will be
seen in the report referred to, that the influence
of the considerations connected with those laws,

is sufficient to control the decision on nearly
every question of location that will arise in the
establishment of the work.

Though these laws appear exceedingly obvious and simple, after the attention has once
been properly drawn to the subject, my intercourse with persons whose occupation ought to
render them familiar with their consequences,
has convinced me that the ideas of the best in-
formed in relation to the circumstances by
which the value and efficiency of an improvement are governed, are generally vague and un-
satisfactory.   And I have ventured to hope that
the publication of these reflections might be
useful in correcting some popular errors in relation to such subjects, and be especially ser-
viceable in the prosecution of the important
enterprise with which you are charged.

I am, gentlemen, very respectfully,
your obedient servant,

CHARLES ELLET, Jr.

INTRODUCTION.

The frequency of discussions, and the general assertion of opinions on the most important questions considered in these pages, might appear to render superfluous
any attempt, at this day, to throw new light on the subject. But believing that the views usually taken of the
LAWS OF TRADE, are too comprehensive to be received
with confidence, and that many principles asserted as
axioms, have not been sufficiently analyzed to be established as such, the author has endeavored to reduce the
subject to a shape that would adapt it to a more rigid examination.

In doing this, it has been his object to trace the different divisions of which the trade of a great line is chiefly
composed, to some of their most obvious and important
consequences; and especially to show, in almost every
aspect of the subject, to what extent the trade and revenue of an improvement are functions of the charges for
the conveyance of the commodities carried on the line:
and finally, to point out the effects of changes in the conditions of the trade, by which the merit of a route is in-

fluenced—the effect of increased or diminished facilities
of communication on the tonnage of the work, and the
profits derived from its transportation.

The trade of the Ohio being the most important object of the competition of the principal lines of improvements of this country; and withal, the immediate aim
of the particular enterprise under the professional charge
of the writer, has been selected as the most convenient
and proper for special applications of the results of the
investigation.

During the years of the author's connexion with the
JAMES RIVER AND KANAWHA IMPROVEMENT, he has
found himself called upon, frequently, either to propose
measures of some importance to the company, or to take
an active part in the support of particular questions which
have arisen from time to time in the progress of the
work, and in which his sentiments have differed from
those entertained by other friends of the project. And
in the course of this investigation, those questions are
adverted to, for the purpose of elucidation of analytical formulæ, or because, as objects of interest, they naturally occurred to his attention; and likewise, sometimes, because the opportunity was afforded to him to
show, in the peculiar laws of trade, additional motives
for the adoption of the measures which he has advocated.

The nature of the subject has made it essential to the convenient and concise demonstration of the principles which are the objects of the research, to admit the introduction of mathematical formulæ throughout the investigation. The writer may appear to have used this method of conveying his ideas, and exposing results in cases where a more popular mode might have been as conveniently practised. But, besides that these facts are generally connected with others that could not be adequately demonstrated differently, having to introduce such expressions for some purposes, it was deemed as well to profit by their precision in others, where it could perhaps have been as easily avoided.

As the mathematics employed is, however, of a very elementary character, it can offer no impediment to any but the youngest professional reader. All investigations that would not be available for objects of practical pursuit, or that would merely offer opportunity for a display of science, have been of course avoided.

The writer is daily and hourly in the midst of practical men, and unremittingly engaged in the preparation or execution of plans of practical utility; and has no time to devote to subjects which are not entirely apposite to the pursuits with which he is constantly occupied.

But, although the demonstrations will be sufficiently evident to the reader who is at all familiar with analytical transformations, it will not be inappropriate to repeat here, in a more popular form, the course of argument pursued, and some of the most remarkable of the results to which it leads.

One of the primary objects of the examination is, to determine the value of the trade of the Ohio and Mississippi rivers, in relation to its transportation on lines of artificial communication, and the circumstances connected with the improvements contending for it, by which its value is liable to be influenced.

It is assumed as the basis of the investigation, that the owner of any property destined for exportation, residing between the junction of the improvement in question with the Ohio, and New Orleans, will have to select the route by which he shall transmit his merchandise, from that presented by those rivers, and those of the numerous artificial channels crossing the states between the western waters and the Atlantic. That in making his election, he puts his estimate in dollars, on all the circumstances influencing his choice, and, among others, on the cost of transportation of the commodity to be forwarded.

This cost of transportation is, in one direction, the charge for freight down the Ohio and Mississippi; and in the other, the charge for freight up to the beginning of the improvement; the charge for freight on the improvement; and finally, the charge for toll for the benefit he receives from the work.

Of these charges, the only one over which the directors of the improvement have the entire control, is that which represents the profit, or the toll levied for the use of the work.

If, then, any given charge be established, it will be evident on a little inspection, that under this charge, and in view of all the accompanying circumstances, the trade of the Ohio and Mississippi will, for every article sent by those rivers to market, be divided; that that situated at the terminus of the work will be drawn to the east, and that the portion which is near the mouth of the river will find its way to New Orleans: and, further, that there will be, somewhere between the improvement and the Gulf of Mexico, a line of separation, or dividing point, which marks the place from which the trade in any commodity commences to flow in opposite directions.

If, in this state of things, the charge for toll on the line should receive any increase, while all the other divisions of the tax on the trade remain stationary, it is apparent that this dividing point would be moved higher up the river, and that in consequence of the change, a greater amount of trade would descend to New Orleans, and a smaller amount would pass over the work. It is clear that the operation of this increase of toll would exclude a certain portion of the trade from the line; but it does not follow that this diminution of tonnage would be productive of a corresponding diminution of revenue; for the charge levied upon the remaining trade is higher than before—and consequently, the profit derived from each ton that passes is greater, and compensates, more or less, for the decrease of quantity.

Now, if the charge for toll be supposed to go on increasing, until the dividing point is forced up the river quite to the improvement, the whole of the trade would be excluded from the work and drawn off by the river— and there would consequently be no revenue. If, on the contrary, the charge for toll were diminished, the dividing point would be transferred to a still lower position in the valley; the trade would in this case go on increasing; and if the charge were reduced to nothing, or the article were subjected only to the charge for freight, it would be greater than under any other arrangement, but the dividend due to its passage would again be zero.

There is, then, some intermediate point where there will be a finite charge levied, and a certain quantity of merchandise will be conveyed, and where the combined influence of the two will produce the greatest possible revenue.

To determine this charge, and the value of the trade and profit due to it, is a part of the object of these pages. But, for the purpose of the investigation, it is essential to know the positions in which the trade of the Ohio is brought into that river, and the quantities that are delivered at those points. These, however, are data which we cannot obtain for the purpose of a general solution; and it is necessary, in the absence of positive information, to supply their place by an hypothesis.

The hypothesis assumed to make up for this deficiency, is the simplest, and I believe the nearest the actual
state of things that can be made; and supposes, as the
prevailing law of the distribution of tonnage, that equal
quantities are furnished in equal distances.

Although this is not positively true, it would appear to
be, at first sight, most probably a near approximation to the
truth : and one of the results of the investigation, goes to
show that a very great difference might exist between
this assumption and the facts of the case, without producing any essential modification of the results. But, independently of this demonstration, by which is established
the applicability of the formulæ to the practical purpose
of determining the most expedient toll to levy, I feel
assured that whatever principle is sustained in the pre-
sumption that twice as much tonnage will pass over a
work which receives all the trade that is found in a space
of two hundred miles of the valley of the Ohio, as over
one which receives the trade of but half that distance, or
one hundred miles, will not be rejected, because it might
obtain a little more or a little less than twice as much.

These preliminary points being established, one of the
first consequences which flow from them is, that when a
work is operating most advantageously for the pecuniary
interest of its proprietors, the charge for toll must be just
half as great as that charge which would exclude the
whole trade from the line; and that when this toll is

levied, the distance from which the article will be drawn up the river to the work, or sent down the river from it, will be just half the distance to which it would be carried if no toll at all were exacted.

The continuation of the examination unfolds other facts equally simple and not less important.

We find among other consequences, that if the charges are so arranged that the work is operating to the best advantage, and any circumstance occur to modify the charge for freight, a new tariff should be established to adapt the work to the new condition of things: that if the charge for freight be increased, the tonnage passing over the line will be diminished—and that to bring it back again to the point required by the condition of a maximum revenue, the toll must be diminished; and that the amount of this reduction of toll must be just half the augmentation of freight. That the effect of any increase of the cost of freight will be to augment the whole tax for the transportation of the article just half the value of this increase, and diminish the charge for toll, or profit per ton, precisely the same amount.

The quantity of tonnage and the revenue of the work are both diminished by this operation; and the solution teaches us that the amount of the loss of revenue—independently of the increased tax on the owners of the property—is, for small changes, equal to that which would be found by multiplying the whole tonnage by the length of the line, and by the increase of the charge for freight.

In pursuing the argument, we are led by the most convincing considerations, to an easy mode of testing the correctness of the charges levied for the use of the improvement by the actual results on the line ; an examination which establishes, that when the condition that the toll exacted is the most advantageous is complied with, its value must be equal to twice the charge for freight on the river, multiplied by the ratio which the greatest distance the article is brought up the river to the work, bears to the length of the line of the improvement.

This result conducts us on to a simple mode of correcting the charge, if it be found not to comply with the conditions of the test.

The application of these principles leads us to other consequences of the utmost importance in the location and establishment of the plan of any improvement. It shows that if a choice of lines is presented, of which the claims are equal in other respects, but which differ in length, there will generally be cause, as we know, for a preference to be given to the shorter. That the amount of this preference will be—besides a direct pecuniary advantage, equal to the whole cost of sending the whole trade of the line over the unnecessary space, which is otherwise apparent—the value of a certain increase of trade, of which the measure is expressed, and the additional impulse to the business of the country that would spring from its possession.

An easy extension of the argument proves, that if for one improvement it be proposed to substitute another of the same length, for a portion of the distance, on which the cost of freight would be higher, while all other circumstances remain permanent, there will be a positive loss of revenue equal to the cost of transporting the whole tonnage of the work over the distance for which the substitution is made, at a price equal to the difference in the charges for freight on the two works respectively.

The importance of this consideration to those companies whose improvements are a combination of rail roads and canals, in urging the extension of the water parts of their lines to the highest practicable point, is adverted to, and familiar examples are adduced in evidence.

Finally, it is shown that whatever increases the cost of transportation, at the same time diminishes the tonnage, and deprives the treasury of the improvement of a revenue equal to the whole increase of the cost of transporting the trade; and that whatever increases the permanent relative standing of a market on the line, increases the revenue for every article sent to the market, an amount at least equal to the additional sum for which the article is sold.

These results are arrived at in the course of investigations having other objects in view; and are dwelt upon incidentally with more care, and their importance illustrated more by examples, than may appear to be demanded by objects so apparent. It is done, however, in the belief that millions have been expended on the works of this country, without the admission, or knowledge of the fact, that, generally, *whatever unnecessary tax is levied on the trade, is at least so much deducted from the revenue of the improvement.*

Such are among the most prominent results of the investigation; and whatever faults may be discerned in the imperfect mode of treating the subject, the great importance of its object will be readily admitted.

This object is no less than the determination of the laws that govern the trade for which the most active competition is at this moment maintained, or shortly to occur, between all the states east of the Alleghany, from New York to Mississippi; and the vast anticipated amount of which, has already caused the actual expenditure for internal improvements east of the Ohio and the Lakes, of more than NINETY MILLIONS OF DOLLARS, and to the attainment of which there is already pledged a much greater additional sum.

But, immense as is the interest involved in such enterprises, the fact is not the less certain, that the laws on which their success is mainly dependant, have rarely, if ever received a passing notice, either from the professional engineer, or from the statesmen in whose energy the efforts of such corporations have originated.

No subject has been more singularly neglected, in examinations of the policy of internal improvements, than this; and it is far from unusual to find in the report of the same engineer, one system of improvement preferred over another, for reasons deemed adequate in the document, without one reference to the influence which the difference of the charges on the two lines would have on the quantities which they would respectively convey.

He will frequently estimate the cost of the improvement on which it becomes his duty to report, with the utmost seeming accuracy, and pretend to set down the value of every item to the fraction of a dollar; will estimate the trade which the work will receive, and the consequent revenue and probable dividend, with equal care; but rarely, if ever, notice the influence of the charges on the line itself which are to produce the revenue, upon the tonnage from which it is to be drawn.

He estimates, and seems to compare the costs and merits of different lines of unequal lengths and various properties, without once adverting to the influence which the length and cost of transportation will have on the amount of freight and on the profit per ton, and consequently on the dividend itself.

Indeed, there is no part of the profession to which the attention of engineers has been so little directed, and for the advancement of which so little has been done. The minds of professional men seem to have been so exclusively directed to the pursuit of the laws of construction, that they have neglected entirely the object for which their constructions are intended.

It is more than probable that this neglect of the primary subject for the study of those who are interested in the success of public improvements,—and of all the questions which occupy their attention, the one most worthy of their investigation—is partly to be ascribed to the apparent irregularity of the distribution of trade, which might seem, at the first glance, to put at defiance any attempt to reduce it to the order necessary for the application of the principles of an exact science.

But this irregularity, as is adequately demonstrated in the volume, is more imaginary than real; and the hypothesis from which a portion of the deductions are obtained, is simpler, and more worthy of reliance, than those on which the most important theories of the profession, and many of physics are based. Compared with the most approved theory of the *Equilibrium of Arches ;* the most refined investigation of the stability of *Revêtements,* and the *Poussée des Terres,* or even with some of the safest principles of hydraulics, it is believed the candid reader will acknowledge, that the annunciations of many of the LAWS OF TRADE here offered, are the most rigorous.

And it is probable that the engineer who might wish to determine the proper dimensions for a canal proposed to be enlarged, would find himself less embarrassed in establishing the increase of trade and revenue which would follow a given reduction of the charge for freight, than

the increase of water-way adequate to produce that reduction.

But, by indulging in these statements, the author may
be thought to encroach on the prerogative of the professional reader, whose province it is to pass his own judg-
ment on these points.

He resigns the subject into the hands of such readers,
in the confident belief that the imperfections of his
method of treating it will be corrected, and that it will
receive the extension and improvement which he thinks
it merits at their hands. He ventures to hope, too,
that they of the number who are accustomed to the dis-
charge of severe daily duties, arising, as in his case,
from the necessity of superintending a line in the progress
of rapid construction under a force of nearly 4,000 men—
and conducting at the same time the survey of a mixed
line of more than 300 miles in length—will admit that
it is hardly to be expected that much attention could be
bestowed on the arrangement and style of the production,
and that they will therefore grant some indulgence in
consideration of the circumstances under which the
volume is produced.

What was deemed essential to the object, it is hoped,
has received sufficient care to be rendered distinct and exact; and for the rest, he has done as well as he found to
be practicable, in a work that was written in almost every
tavern on the line between Richmond and the Ohio, and in
a manuscript that is sent from his saddle-bags to the press.

PART I.

GENERAL LAWS OF TRADE.

SECTION I.

OF THE PRINCIPLE OF TRADE.

1. The regulating principle of trade is the desire of gain. Whether we regard the subject in relation to the principles which govern the commercial intercourse between distant nations, or in reference to the more confined views recognized in the limited transactions of individuals, we will find it to be founded on the hope of profit. And however comprehensive may be the view taken of the question, when analyzed, it will be discovered that the active principle of trade—whether of states or of incorporated institutions—may be at once reduced to the simple feeling that prompts to the efforts of private enterprise.

The action of a great institution is but the united action of the individual voices, dictated by common individual interests, of which it is constituted.

This principle is the very life of internal improvements. The patrons and proprietors of any line are the individuals whose property is to be enhanced in value, or whose reputations, valued perhaps more highly than property, are to be elevated by its success. And the direction of the voice of each party for or against the undertaking, is the result of a more or less complicated calculation of the chances for that party to become a gainer by the enterprise.

2. But after a work is accomplished, and trade has commenced flowing upon the line, a new condition of things has place, and new calculations have to be instituted.

No work can be constructed in an improved country, without meeting with a rival; and the result of the competition which arises between such improvements, is nothing else than the resultant of the calculations of the chances of gain of all the individuals who use the improvements as a means of transacting their business.

In every department of the occupations of civilized life, such a calculation is attempted, and the decision of each individual is made to depend on the character of the balance.

The merchant who makes a foreign importation, goes through the investigation, and determines to what state or what city he shall transmit his order ; and one of his data is the cost of freight, another the terms of purchase, a third the duties, a fourth the commissions; in fact, every thing on which a determination of the expense of obtaining, and the value of his goods when received, is intended to be taken into the account.

The farmer who sends his plough to the smith for repair, makes a similar reckoning in determining to what shop to send it; and not a share is sharpened, or coulter pointed, that does not give rise to such a computation, and that is not sent to the anvil which is supposed to combine the greatest amount of advantages.

3. To render more palpable the influence of this consideration of profit in the effect which it has on the competition and success of rival public improvements, we will refer to the sketch in the plate, fig. 1. There are here represented two primary lines of improvements, situated at a considerable distance from each other, and connected together by numerous roads and secondary works of various descriptions.

We may suppose at first, that all the trade of the country in the immediate vicinity of these rivals, is accommodated by the line on which it is situated; and that that of the intervening district is in some manner or other divided between them.

If we start, then, from one improvement, and proceed towards the other, along either of the connecting branches R, R, we shall find that the inhabitants in the vicinity of A send their produce to market by that line, and obtain their supplies from the city at which it terminates; and that those in the neighborhood of B find it their interest to patronize the line B and city B. But in passing further, we come to a point, a, at which the claims of the two works are regarded as nearly equal;

and here we will find that the population to the left of a go to A, and to the right to B ; and that just at this point there are a few who deal alternately or indiscriminately at both places—who take advantage, perhaps, of the fluctuations of the market at either city, and divide their custom between them.

This dividing point is determined by the calculations of the parties themselves, who take into consideration the cost of reaching both improvements, the charges on the improvements, and the advantages, as markets, of the cities at which they respectively terminate.

The same fact is true of the other connecting lines, and of the roads that connect other improvements with these ; and is applicable to every position in the country, and to every road that is traversed by any species of conveyance.

If we take into consideration all the connecting or lateral roads, RR, R'R', &c. we shall obtain a series of points, a, a', a'', a''', &c. through which is drawn the dotted line a, a', &c. in the figure.

These points represent places in the line which divides the trade between the rival improvements.

4. If, in this state of things, something should occur to change the relative advantages of the routes, the result of the calculations of the people residing in the intervening country would undergo a corresponding modification.

If, for example, the market at A were from any cause to improve, while that at B remained stationary ; or the cost of transportation on A were to fall, while on B it continued constant, or was increased, it is evident that the dividing points, a, a', a'', &c., would no longer exhibit the positions where the two lines would offer equal attractions, but that there would be a difference between the two, at these points, in favor of A ; and that the dividing point previously found at a, would be transferred to b, that at a' to b', and so on.

The direction in which the trade is carried, is for every article the result of a computation, and this result must vary with the changes in the values of the elements which constitute the data of the problem. Every commodity intended for market, which will bear the charge for transportation to each point of sale, is subjected to these considerations. It will be forwarded either to one place or the other, and the place to which it will be sent, will be determined by the combination of all the advantages and objections attached to both ; and whatever increases the relative advantage of any line over its rival, will likewise increase its trade at the expense of its competitor.

5. There is, however, another class of commodities of great importance in the economy of public improvements, to which these considerations are not so applicable.

There are many heavy products of the earth which will bear but a limited charge for transportation, and consequently will often not sustain the cost of carriage from the dividing point to the terminus of either work. The

stone, lumber, ore and coal will frequently be found to
belong to this division ; and if the charge upon these and
other similar articles exceed a certain limit, they will be
entirely excluded from the lines.   Under a given charge,
such commodities will be carried some distance, which
the experience of the particular line will determine; but
if the charge be reduced, or the demand become greater,
and the value of the commodity higher, this distance will
receive a corresponding augmentation ; and if the charge
be increased, or the value of the material diminished, the
distance which it will be carried along the improvement
will be simultaneously reduced.

6. The distance in the interior from which the article
will be brought laterally to the line, is affected by the
same circumstances.   The whole charge for carriage
which it is able to bear, is known from experiment ; and
if the cost of transporting it along the line B, from R to
the city B, be less than the whole tax which it is capable
of sustaining, there will be a certain residuum at R which
may be appropriated to its carriage from or to the interior.
The distance n R from which it will be brought, will be
proportional to this balance; and consequently, at any
other point R' where a smaller balance remains, the distance R'n' will be less; and it will diminish as we pass
along the line B, until we attain a point, R''', where the
whole charge which the commodity will bear will be consumed in the tax on the line.

7. Similar reasoning applied to the road A, will give

us a series of points, n, n', n'', and teach us that the trade in all such commodities will only be drawn to the improvements from triangular spaces $R'''nR$, on each side of the lines ; and that as much of these articles as may be found in the space intervening between n and n, n' and n', will be entirely shut out of market.

This case, and that previously pointed out, are believed to embrace all the most important objects of the trade of the principal lines of improvement in this country ; and it will be convenient to distinguish between them in the subsequent investigation.

This division of the trade into two distinct classes, as well as its division between rival improvements, is the consequence of particular calculations prompted by a view to gain ; and the results of deductions having that principle for their basis, present the best possible gua- rantee of correctness—the certainty of the accuracy ob- served in the promotion of individual interest.

SECTION II.

COST OF TRANSPORTATION.

8. In the elucidation of the views expressed in these pages, it becomes frequently convenient to illustrate the subject, by the application of the principles of the investi- gation to practical examples. And although the object of the author is not generally to endeavor to obtain results

which possess any other value than that of offering illus-
trations of the subject, it has always been regarded most
expedient to make the examples analogous to the cases
most likely to occur.   For this purpose, it is necessary to
fix the values of the terms of comparison as nearly as is
found to be compatible with the nature of the subject.

The design being in part to illustrate the influence of
internal improvements by the effect which is produced on
the commerce of the country by changes in the price of
transportation, and the extent to which that effect is
dependant on the actual cost of conveyance, it is an
object of some importance to determine this element of
every investigation of the subject, in the most important
cases which we encounter on the works of this country.

9. Unfortunately, the mode in which the transportation on our principal lines of intercommunication is conducted, renders this an object of exceedingly difficult
attainment.   The statements which are published by the
officers of the companies, or by the agents of the states
having the control of public works, are almost without
exception, injudicious in their arrangement, and confused
in the detail; and the reader who looks through those
documents, rarely has an opportunity to congratulate
himself on the discovery of a positive, well authenticated
fact, of which useful application can be made.   Arguments are frequently met with, based upon inadequate
experience, to prove that certain consequences will eventually be realized ; but as these arguments are for the

most part designed to revive the drooping confidence of
the public, or to stimulate the stockholder to a new venture under brighter auspices—and are, withal, sometimes
the productions of minds elated by zeal in favor of an
adopted scheme—they must be received with the allowance due to the estimates of enthusiasm. Such arguments as I advert to have frequently been offered by the
advocates of particular rail roads, and have been as often
found wanting under the test of experiment; and we
are still left, in deciding on a mean value for the cost of
conveyance by this system, to choose between the alternatives of adopting, as a standard of comparison, the
prices anticipated by the ardent friends of works of dubious merit, and those which are furnished by such facts
as we can obtain from the best authenticated reports of
actual experiment.

10. In the calculations presented in these pages, however, I have neither thought it fair to assume, as the
basis of my conclusions, the extravagant hopes of the
friends of particular projects, nor the experience of imperfect specimens of the art.

I believe there is yet no rail road in operation in this
country, on which the business is transacted with the
order and economy which may be eventually expected
on the great thoroughfares between the Atlantic and the
western waters. The lines we have in operation are
generally but indifferently constructed ; and there are
none on which the trade approaches near to their capa-

city for its accommodation; and at the same time, it is only on those works which are in full and regular activity, that we must look for the effects which may be anticipated from the perfection of the system.

In short, neither the roads, nor the power, nor the vehicles of transportation, have attained the limit of probable improvement; and it would be an instance of unusual incredulity, to doubt that the steady perseverance which has brought the steam-engine to its present high degree of perfection, will continue to introduce useful modifications in its form, and in the principle of its motion ; and that the cars will yet be better adapted to the severe service which they undergo, and that the roads will be rendered less liable to derangement.

These are changes which we are justified in regarding as the certain results of experiment, and which authorize us in the assumption of a mean charge for conveyance below that which has been presented by the best works in existence.

11. But still there is a limit beyond which improvement, under the most favorable circumstances, cannot advance. The trade must always be carried over the summit of the road ; the friction can hardly be much reduced ; the oxidation and wear of the rails cannot be diminished ; the influence of time on their durability is unavoidable; the cost of fuel, oil, workmanship, and the expenses of agencies, will continue to increase with the increase of business.

And withal, there are unforeseen and unavoidable contingencies which will ever interfere to prevent the practical attainment of the measure of perfection of which the system is in effect susceptible.

12. The chief sources from which we have a right to anticipate a reduction of the charge for transportation on our present roads, *at the present rates of speed*, are in the repairs of the road and carriages, and the cost of fuel.

The work may be made more permanent, by being made more costly, or more judiciously ; but when we reflect on the extent of the improvement in the construction of common roads, from the establishment of the Roman ways to the completion of the best works of Great Britain, we shall hardly find encouragement to hope for any material change, in this respect, in the formation of the road bed. And if we regard the modifications which the superstructure of rail roads has undergone since the first employment of cast iron for the purpose, in the year 1767, at Colebrookdale ; and compare those early attempts with the common practice of this country at this time, we shall scarce venture to look for a very great reduction in this item of annual expenditure.

The art of making cars has been quite well understood for some 3,000 years ; and though there are some advantages possessed by the English coach over the Roman chariot, it may be questioned whether the difference in the cost of repairs, and the power required for their movement, hold out grounds for the anticipation of any great changes, in these particulars, in the modern rail road car for the next few centuries.

The cost of fuel constitutes but a small portion of the aggregate bill of expenses for the maintenance of the business of a line of rail road transportation; and the moderate reduction which we may look for in this item, can have no serious influence on the result.

13. On the whole, while I do not doubt that our best existing roads are susceptible of a more economical management than they have yet received, and that an increase of business will generally be attended by a corresponding reduction of the cost of transportation, and that something may be hoped for from the progress of improvement, I am not prepared to believe that while the present velocity is maintained, the influence of these considerations is destined soon to be very extensively felt. More has been anticipated from the increase of business, than can reasonably be expected to be realized; for though the annual expenses do in fact consist of two distinct classes—those that are fixed, and independant of the amount of the business done on the line, and those which increase with the increase of trade—they may still be regarded, for all the most important lines, as nearly proportional, on the same work, to the amount of tonnage.

If we make such a division of the charges, that part which expresses the fixed expenses, or the expenses due to a very small business, added to the annual deterioration of the work attributable to the perishable nature of the materials employed in its construction, will be found to be, when compared with the aggregate expenditures on a line doing a considerable business, an exceedingly small item.

If the trade were very light, then the ratio of the constant to the variable charges would well deserve attention; but the relative importance of the former will always diminish as the value of the business, and consequently the variable expenditures, increase.

14. It is far from my intention to contend, in these remarks, against the probability of a very great reduction of the expense of rail road transportation. On the contrary, I am of opinion that there is wide room for improvement in many parts of the arrangement of our roads, and the system of haulage applied to them.

It appears to me, that a radical error of the present method, is the constant effort to transmit merchandise with the high velocity demanded by the impatience of the travelling community. That to attain this object, the engines are forced to operate with but partial loads; their number is consequently unnecessarily multiplied, the wear and tear of the road and vehicles—both because of the greater number of engines and the speed maintained— is excessive, and the annual charges are, of course, proportionally high.

There is no particular reason assigned for the attempt

to carry merchandise at a speed of 15 or even 20 miles per hour, excepting that the improvements of the machine have given us the power to move at that rate, and those in the management of the works have thought proper to indulge it.

It is a mistake to suppose that the expense of carriage on rail roads, is independant of the velocity of the motion ; and I scarcely doubt that if the subject be fairly investigated, it will be found that it increases with the increase of speed almost as rapidly as in the case of transportation by water. And to bring the cost of carriage nearer to the limit which is known to have place on canals, we must bring the speed of the car nearer to that which is permitted to the canal boat.

15. There is also another source of expense, resulting in part from the preceding, that might be dispensed with. It is the charge incident to the maintainance of a double track.

There are very few roads in the country where the double track is at all essential ; but there are very few extensive lines in operation, or projected, where a provision for it has not been made.

Doubtless, the practice is the result of imitation. The English roads were made double, where the conveyance was expected to consist chiefly of passengers, the merchandise was valuable, and at a time when the load of an engine on light grades was 25 or 30 tons.

Our situation, in America, is different. The country

itself is broader, our lines are longer, the chief exports are heavier, and success depends wholly on reducing the cost of transportation. For this object, I think we must increase the strength of our roads, and the weight of our engines; and by reducing the velocity, enable them to carry such trains as will render frequent passing unnecessary, and consequently permit the rejection of the superfluous track.

The present tonnage of the Erie Canal might be conveniently carried on such a rail road, if the grades were not more abrupt than could be obtained in the country through which that work passes.

The cost of the mere superstructure of a single track designed to be permanent, and for the accommodation of a heavy business, cannot be estimated at less than $12,000 per mile ; and if to this we add, for the additional cost of grading for a double track, $6,000 per mile, we have the sum of $18,000 per mile for the difference between the cost of a single and double road.

The interest on this sum, at 6 per cent, is $1,080 per per annum.

If we assume $500 per mile for the annual charge for keeping in repair the additional track, we shall have $1,580 per mile for the whole annual expense of its maintenance.

We should, then, in the construction of a rail road from the Atlantic to the Ohio, which we may suppose to be 500 miles in length, save the sum of $9,000,000 in its first cost—the interest on that capital, or $540,000 per annum, of course—and the additional sum of $250,000 for the annual expenses, by the suppression of a track, which is strictly superfluous.

That such a road would generally be sufficient, I shall prove elsewhere ;* at present, I think I may safely assert, that by the expedients proposed—the rejection of one track and the reduction of the velocity,—and the saving incident to both, we shall not fail to accomplish the object in view—that of greatly reducing the cost of transporting the heavy products of the country.

16. To fix, accurately, the value of rail road transportation for any future period, is no easy matter; but it may be obtained for various roads in active operation at this time, with an approach to accuracy; and I think it will not be denied that the mean value which I have assumed for it in these pages, is quite as low as is warranted by the experience of the country, if not of the prospects of future improvements.

In the investigation of this subject with reference to canals, although there is still some deficiency of data, the evidence is sufficient to enable us to establish, the average charge in question with as much precision as could be expected, in assuming a mean of quantities liable to so much variation.   And if there be any objection to the value which I have attributed to this item, it must be that it is rather above than below the truth.

* See Appendix.

The cost of transportation on common turnpikes is liable to variations which take a much wider range. And, in consequence, I have preferred to divide these roads into two classes; the one offering a firm and even surface to the wheel, as the McAdam and some other systems, and the other such impediments as are met with in the more common and imperfect routes of this country.

17. The nature of these investigations has rendered it essential, as well as convenient, to separate the charges which are levied upon articles conveyed by either system of improvement, into two distinct divisions. The first, for the sake of adhering to established terms, I call *freight*, and include in it every charge to which the article is liable, excepting that which I designate as *toll*. By the second, or *toll*, I mean to represent only the profit to the proprietors of the work on the article conveyed. Consequently, when the freight on a ton of goods passing over a rail road is spoken of, it is intended that the expression shall cover the salaries of all the officers and agents engaged on the work; the expense of maintaining the cars and motive power, the cost of repairs, and renewal of the road, &c.; and when the word toll is used, it is to be regarded as the profit on the conveyance of that ton exclusive of all other charges, and is consequently synonymous with the *dividend* per ton per mile, to the stockholder, on the object conveyed.

18. With this understanding of the meaning of the

term, I assume for the mean cost of *freight,* for heavy
goods [see Appendix] on

Canals, 1¼ cents per ton per mile,

Rail roads, 2½   "   "   "

McAdam roads, 10 to 15   "

Common turnpikes, 15 to 20   "

Steamboats on the lakes, 2 to 4   "

Steamboats on the Ohio and Mississippi, ½ to 1½ ; future average, ¾ of a cent per ton per mile.

SECTION III.

OF THE DISTRIBUTION OF TONNAGE.

19. In attempting to reduce the subject of internal
commerce to a system adapted to the application of mathematical reasoning, it is necessary to determine, or assume, the position and mode of distribution of the products of the country, which are expected to constitute the
trade.   At the first view, this branch of the subject appears to be involved in much difficulty.   The varieties
and localities of the articles which are liable to be carried
on lines of internal improvement are so numerous, and
the productiveness of the soil so unequal, that it would
seem scarcely practicable to generalize, without subject-
ing ourselves to the risk of frequent deception.

If the object were to obtain positive quantities for the expression of the value of an improvement, passing through a district of which the resources were supposed to be known, this difficulty would not be altogether imaginary. But, even in this case, it would be quite possible, by a sufficient devotion to the subject, to obtain results as satisfactory, and as well deserving of confidence as in many other departments of practical science.

There are certain relations between the toll which is levied, the cost of carriage, and the trade which depends on them; between the length of the line and the dividends of the work; between different systems under different or similar circumstances, quite within the reach of general investigations.

A careful study of the country supplying the trade, and the conditions by which its value is influenced, will furnish the data necessary for the confident application of such principles.

20. But, although to investigate each particular question with strict accuracy, we must learn in what manner the tonnage comes upon the line, in what proportions it is distributed along the route, and the places of its destination; we may, for the purpose of more general comparisons, assume these facts to be given.

In this view, I have made what I deem to be, in general, the most probable, and frequently a very accurate supposition.

I consider that in a long line of improvement, such as

any of the principal routes leading from the seaboard to the western waters, the quantities of most articles of commerce passing on the work, are proportional to the area of country from which they are obtained, or to which they are transmitted. Consequently, the heavy trade, as well as that which is obtained in the competition with a rival, which is received on the work, is, for every point on the route, proportional to the lateral distance it is transported to the improvement. And supposing the whole space between two rival improvements to be drained by the lateral roads which traverse it, the area of the country accommodated by each road will be proportional to the distance which the commodity is transported along it, and the distance to the right and left of the road, or parallel with the line of the improvement, from which it is carried to the road.

21. Many public improvements terminate on the borders of a lake or river, where there is an existing navigation with which other improvements communicate. Several of the primary lines now in progress of construction in this country, are of this description ; and a considerable portion of these pages is applied to those works.

In strict regard to the division which has been made of the articles constituting the objects of trade, the same considerations which have been applied to the country traversed by the improvement itself, should be extended to the navigation with which it communicates. But as, in general, the length of these works is so great that the heavy and cheap commodities of traffic are, for the greater part, completely excluded when required to pass over the whole line, I have usually neglected them in the investigation of this branch of the subject, and regarded the trade which traverses the entire route as proportional to the distance from which it is brought to the improvement.

For example, in estimating the tonnage of any article brought up the valley of the Ohio to the work, I regard that valley as the recipient of the produce of a belt of country of uniform width and equal productiveness, as far as the article in question is found upon it; and consequently, for every mile of that stream of which the improvement can command this commodity, it will receive an equal number of tons.

22. It is presumed hardly necessary to say that there are many exceptions to the applicability of this law of distribution of tonnage, and that even in the best established cases, it is not strictly correct. If we mark off mile by mile of a line of rail road, and note the number of tons of plaster, bales of goods, and pounds of groceries that are taken from the cars; and the number of cords of wood, bushels of wheat, or barrels of pork that are received upon them from each space, we shall observe considerable differences between the results and those which would be given by the law assumed.

But if we make the divisions at spaces of ten, or twenty, or fifty miles, and compare the results, we will find them to approximate much more closely to the supposition.

It is not contended that each mile on the Ohio and Mississippi receives an equal number of tons of produce, or gives employment to an equal number of horses power for the movement of the steamboats that carry it off. But it is believed that if we could compare accurately the trade of divisions of 100 miles, we would consider them not to differ too widely for the admission of my views on the subject. We would find, in proceeding from Pittsburg down the river, that the first space includes the towns of Beaver, Wellsburg, Steubenville and Wheeling ; the second, Marietta and Parkersburg ; the third, the entrances of the Guyandotte, Great Kanawha, and Hockhocking rivers ; the fourth, Portsmouth and Maysville ; the fifth, Cincinnati ; and the sixth, Louisville, &c.; and I doubt not, that if the equal value of the trade of these divisions be not admitted, the investigations offered in the following sections will show that the deviations from that law are not too great for the use that is made of the hypothesis.*

23. In short, the supposition is nearer the actual condition of things than any other that we can make ; and is that which the mind of every one immediately assumes in reflecting upon the chances of success of a projected improvement.

* See §5, Part iii.

It is a supposition which approaches to the truth ; and in the comparison of one system with another under that assumption, the departure from truth influences both works nearly in the same manner. Besides, the error of the supposition in one point for a given commodity, will be positive, and at another negative ; and the articles which constitute the trade of an improvement are so numerous, that any error which may be committed in relation to one, besides being in itself necessarily small, will apply to so small a portion of the aggregate revenue, as to have no sensible influence on the prosperity of the line.

24. It is in fact of indefinite quantities of this sort that the materials of many of the calculations of the engineer are composed ; and he must often choose between the alternatives of making the best use he can of the best data he can obtain, or of hazarding a guess based on no principle whatever.

In expressing his views of the propriety of attempting the construction of an improvement designed to vent the products of a district of country, he not only estimates the tonnage which the work will receive, and the points at which it will be obtained and discharged ; but he frequently estimates the cost of the work from data scarcely more certain, the revenue anticipated from the trade, the future decay of materials, cost of repairs and adminis-tration, and finallly, the probable value of the investment.

His calling requires him to go further, and estimate

the tonnage which will be received on his canal, and
the consumption of water which it will require in its
passage through the locks; and sometimes the supply
that will be afforded by the clouds, the area on which
it will fall, the quantity of evaporation from the surface,
the soakage through the pores of the earth, and the
uncertain and indeterminate loss from leakage.

Such estimates are made the basis of large investments,
and every branch of it requires the adoption of positive
quantities. In the matter before us, we generally need
only relative quantities to produce positive results; and
the single objectionable part of the data is the assumption
of an equal number of tons upon an equal number of
square miles.

The productiveness of the country does not affect the
correctness of the argument; and it will be sufficiently
demonstrated in its proper place, that even the supposition
of an uniform distribution of tonnage may differ widely
from the fact, without seriously impairing the correctness
of the conclusions.

SECTION IV.

OF THE DIRECTION OF THE LINE BY WHICH TRADE IS BROUGHT TO THE IMPROVEMENT.

25. After the commencement of a line of internal improvement, one of the first questions for the population

for whose benefit it is to be made, is the determination of the routes along which the commodities constituting its trade are to be carried.

The principle which governs the decision in this matter, is still that of economy; and every party interested will pursue the route by which the whole cost of the transportation of his wares is the least.

A general solution of the problem can aid but little in the establishment of an improvement, or of the branches leading to it; but it will show the results of the particular calculations which are made in determining the most advantageous route, and lead to other conclusions that are worthy of observation.

26. For the purpose of the investigation, we will suppose the line of the improvement to be represented by AB, fig. 2; and designate by

y the least distance CD from the position of any commodity in the interior to the line;

x the distance DE from the foot of the perpendicular CD, to the junction of the lateral road with the improvement;

ε the cost of transportation per ton per mile on the improvement;

β the cost of transportation per ton per mile on the lateral road CE; and

h the distance DA from the nearest point at which the commodity could reach the improvement, to the place for which it is destined.

Then the whole cost of carriage from C to A, by the route CEA, will be represented by

$$\varphi = (x^2 + y^2)^{\frac{1}{2}} \beta + (h - x) \epsilon \, ;$$

and it will always be the object of the persons using the work, to join their road with it in the manner that will reduce this cost to the lowest amount.

27. To determine the value of x, and consequently the angle which the lateral road would form with the direction of the line, we must obtain the condition that will render this expression a maximum. By applying the rules of the differential calculus, we shall have

$$\frac{d \varphi}{d x} = \frac{x \beta}{(x^2 + y^2)^{\frac{1}{2}}} - \epsilon = 0 \, ;$$

from whence we obtain, for the distance in question,

$$x = y \frac{\epsilon}{(\beta^2 - \epsilon^2)^{\frac{1}{2}}} . \qquad (1)$$

28. We will perceive, from this equation, that as the cost of transportation on the lateral road becomes greater than that on the improvement, the angle formed by the directions of the two lines approaches more nearly to a right angle; and that when the charges are equal on the branch, and on the principal line, the angle disappears, and the distance to their junction becomes infinite.

This teaches us at once the importance, in this view of

the subject, of diminishing the cost of freight upon any line of improvement which is to be supplied with trade from lateral branches ; for the lower the charge is made on the improvement the greater is the distance along it that any commodity destined for, or received from the interior, will be carried.

It teaches us further, that a common road in an improved country cannot draw to it the trade and travel from any considerable distance ; because other such roads, destined to the same point, will offer a shorter route and a lower charge than could be obtained by diverging to the former.

For the same reason, a line of rail road will seldom present attractions to any other rail road of great length to join it; since, as soon as the length of the proposed lateral work becomes sufficient to insure it support from the resources of the country, it is likely to be found most advantageous to its proprietors to convert it into a rival, and direct it at once to the point where the produce is to be forwarded.

29. If in the preceding equation, we substitute for β the cost of transportation by a McAdam road, and for ς the freight on a canal, which (neglecting the toll) we will suppose are to each other in the proportion of 1 to 8, we shall have for the distance that any article would be deflected from the position at which the shortest route to the improvement would bring it, nearly,

$$x = \tfrac{1}{8} y \; ;$$

or, an object situated at C, fig. 2, would reach the work at a distance DE from the point nearest to C, equal to a very little more than one eighth the distance from C to the line.

If the line were a rail road, and its branch similar to the preceding, the ratio of their respective charges for freight might be considered as 1 to 4, and this distance would consequently be increased to, nearly

$$x = \tfrac{26}{100} y.$$

I am not to be understood to wish to convey the impression that such would necessarily be the direction of these lateral branches; but merely to indicate the limits towards which they would be likely to incline, for the purpose of showing an additional motive, in the law of trade, for the diminution of the charge for freight.

SECTION V.

OF THE TRADE IN ARTICLES OF SMALL VALUE.

30. I designate in this way, a division of the trade which contributes largely to the revenue of the great improvements of the country, but which is not an object of the competition of rivals.

The staples of the district through which the work passes, have generally sufficient value to attract the exertions of other cities and their improvements; but that extensive class of objects which will not bear the cost of distant transportation, and can therefore only be brought from the country bordering the route, and within a short distance of it, not being affected by the exertions of parallel lines, needs to be separately considered.

The necessity of this division of the business of an improvement, must be apparent; for some articles of consumption will be entirely excluded from market, if taxed beyond a certain limited amount, while others will sustain the cost of carriage to the remotest bounds of civilization.

The stone, lumber and plaster can rarely be brought from any considerable distance, but by the cheapest lines of artificial communication; while peltry, woollens and manufactured iron, will be borne on the back of the hunter a hundred leagues, and repay him, perhaps, for their transportation.

31. On works of moderate extent, or designed for the connexion of two points, where an important trade is already conducted, it may often happen that the division of the tonnage now under discussion is an object of secondary consideration. But on the long lines of this country, which frequently penetrate the wilderness, and look for their support to the forests and petty villages scattered at distant intervals along the route, it cannot be neglected.

In truth, these works are often expected to create the

trade, and to be afterward supported by the trade which
they have created—and this trade in a new country must,
in great part, be constituted of the products of the minerals
and forests in the vicinity of the improvement.

The Erie canal—the work in this country, if not in the
world, which offers the most valuable experience—receives much the greatest portion of its revenue from the
counties bordering the route, and from the trade which
owes its existence to the improvement itself. And notwithstanding the fact that this improvement belongs to
the cheapest known system of inland transportation, and
affords the means of leading the heaviest products of the
field to the principal city and most active sea-port of the
continent; and notwithstanding that it reaches to a chain
of lakes navigated by some hundreds of vessels, and receiving the surplus produce of millions of acres—still this
work yet carries to and from its western extremity but an
insignificant portion of the whole tonnage which it receives. The balance is obtained from the state of New
York, or goes to supply the wants of the citizens of the
state. And it is to a considerable part of that portion of
the trade which constitutes this balance—embracing some
six hundred thousand tons, and paying into the treasury
of New York many hundred thousand dollars per annum—that this division is intended to apply.

32. To investigate this case, we will designate by

Π the charge for carriage which the commodity will
bear ;

ϵ the charge for conveyance per ton per mile, on the improvement, including both freight and toll;

c the charge per ton per mile for toll;

δ the charge per ton per mile for freight;

β the charge on the lateral road; and

h the distance from the point at which the article reaches the line, to that for which it is destined— or the distance it will be carried on the improvement.

Then the sum which this commodity will be taxed on the work, will be

$$h \, \epsilon;$$

and consequently, the additional charge which it will bear in passing to or from the line, will be

$$\pi - h \, \epsilon;$$

and the distance which it will be carried along the lateral road, into the interior, for this sum, will be expressed by

$$\frac{\pi - h\epsilon}{\beta}. \qquad (2)$$

This is evidently the equation of a right line having a certain inclination to that of the improvement.

33. If we suppose the article to be brought from the interior to the terminus A of the work, fig. 3, and consider h to count from this point, it is obvious that the base of the triangle furnishing the trade will be found where h becomes zero, and will consequently be represented by

$$\frac{\Pi}{\beta}; \qquad (3)$$

which shows the greatest distance of inland, or lateral carriage, which the commodity will bear.

The point at which the right line, expressed by equation (2), intersects the improvement, is that where the whole tax which the merchandise will sustain is consumed in the charges upon the work, and where there will be no residue for lateral carriage.

This point will be obtained by making equation (2) equal to zero, and is at the distance

$$h = \frac{\Pi}{\varepsilon}. \qquad (4)$$

This value represents the height of the triangle supplying the improvement with trade; and is the greatest distance that the commodity will be carried along the line.

If we write this equation $\varepsilon = \dfrac{\Pi}{h}$, it will show the limit of the charge which the commodity will bear when transported a distance h; and if we substitute $c + \delta$ in place of ε, we shall obtain

$$c = \frac{\Pi - h\,\delta}{h}$$

for the toll which will exclude those articles from market, which are brought by any branch connecting with the improvement at the distance h.

34. The shape of the country supplying the work with the tonnage which sustains it, is represented in fig. 3, where AD is drawn for the direction of the improvement, and AC, AC are the bases of the triangles, of which the values are expressed above.

We are not, however, to expect the country to assume this form quite from the apex of the triangle to the origin of the work; since the examination of the preceding section shows that the direction of the line of trade will be inclined to that of the improvement, by an angle of which the value depends on the relative cost of transportation on the improvement, and on the roads conducting to it. The shape of the country furnishing the trade will therefore be different, and present the form represented in the same figure by the triangles AC'D; and the produce of the country within the triangles AC'C, will find a market without contributing any thing to the revenue of the improvement.

This consideration will not affect sensibly the correctness of any deductions we may make from the supposition that the tonnage is sent to the line by roads branching off at right angles to it—since the area of this triangle, of which the trade is excluded, is generally small in proportion to that of the whole space; and the error which may exist, will only have an influence on the constant coefficient of the expression of the tonnage, or of the revenue.

We shall continue the examination under this supposition.

35. The area of the country supplying the trade, may be determined directly from equations (3) and (4), and will be found to be represented by

$$\frac{\Pi^2}{\beta \epsilon}; \qquad (5)$$

and if t be put for the number of tons due to each square mile, the mile being the unit of distance, the tonnage furnished by the triangle ACC will be represented by

$$t \frac{\Pi^2}{\beta \epsilon}.$$

From which it appears, that the area of the district which supplies the trade, and the quantity of the trade itself, *are directly proportional to the square of the charge for carriage which the commodity will bear, and inversely as the charge for conveyance on the lateral branches and on the improvement.*

Admitting the hypothesis of uniform productiveness, this result speaks conclusively in favor of the policy of improving the tributaries of any work; since this portion of the tonnage will be increased just in proportion to the diminution of the charge for conveyance on the branches.

Under the same supposition, the aggregate tonnage derived from all the branches will increase just in proportion to the decrease of the cost of conveyance on the improvement itself; a fact which is equally convincing in favor of the diminution of the cost of carriage on the line, or the adoption of that system of improvement, for great works, on which it will be the least.

36. In general applications of these considerations, we are not to forget to give proper attention to the effect of those rival lines which are liable to have an influence on the trade in articles of even very small value, when situated near the origin of the work. We may frequently have to proceed a considerable distance along an improvement, before we find a position where the trade in a commodity will not be affected by competition; and in these cases it would be necessary to apply the formulæ of this section to that portion, and reserve the part nearer the origin of the work for the method which will be given for the trade subject to be drawn off by other improvements.

SECTION VI.

OF THE DIVISION OF TRADE BETWEEN RIVALS.

37. To investigate the law of the trade of an improvement subject to be obtained by a competitor, it will be proper to consider the two works, as before explained, to be connected by numerous roads admitting the pro-

duce to flow in either direction. These roads being independent of each other, and connecting with the improvement at different points, will render it essential to
the economy of the arrangement, to regard them as
independent branches, in establishing the conditions on
which the work shall be used for the transportation of
the trade which they bring to the line.

To determine these conditions for any one branch, or
connecting road, we have not only to ascertain the points
at which it joins with the improvement and its rival,
and the cost of conveying any article in either direction,
but we must learn the relative advantages of the markets at which the commodity may be bought or sold.

Before a farmer forwards his surplus produce, or a
merchant transmits his orders, he estimates, as before
observed, the value of all the objections, and all the advantages offered by the several routes among which he
may choose; and one of the most important subjects
for his consideration, is the merit of the market where he
wishes to buy or sell. He may be able to send his flour
to Richmond, or Philadelphia, or New Orleans, at his
discretion; and in determining, he is governed in part
by the price which flour will command at those points
respectively.

But in speaking of the advantage of one market as
compared with its rival, it is not intended to limit the
expression to the mere question of value obtained by
quotations from the price current. The language is in-

tended to embrace many other considerations, and to indicate the excess of value to the holder of the property, which the commodity will possess, by being delivered at one port instead of another.

38. For the more convenient explanation of our views on this subject, we will designate by

h the distance AR, fig. 1, from the junction of the road RR with our improvement, to the point at which the latter terminates ;

X   the length RR of the connecting road ;

h' the distance BR along the rival, from the junction of the connecting road with it, to its termination ;

x the distance Ra from the improvement A to the point where the trade is divided ;

ϵ the charge per ton per mile, for conveyance on the improvement ;

β the charge on the connecting road ;

ϵ' the charge on the rival, and

M   the value of the superiority of the market at A.

If, now, we regard the charges upon a line as objections to its selection, and the advantage which a rival port presents, an additional objection, it will be sufficient for the determination of the dividing point, to find where the objections to any two lines contending for the same trade, are equal.

In the present case, the objections to the line A are evidently

$$h\,\epsilon + x\,\beta ;$$

and the value of those against the line B, is

$$(X - x)\, \beta + h'\, \epsilon' + M.$$

At the dividing point these two quantities must be equal; and we shall consequently then have the equation

$$h\, \epsilon + x\, \beta = (X - x)\, \beta + h'\, \epsilon' + M\,;$$

from which we obtain immediately, for the position of the line which divides the trade,

$$x = \frac{X\, \beta + h'\, \epsilon' - h\, \epsilon + M}{2\, \beta}. \qquad (6)$$

39. The equation here obtained depends on no hypothesis whatever; and it teaches us, without any qualification, the point from which the trade will flow in opposite directions. The distance of this point from the improvement A measured along the connecting road RR, will be found by deducting the cost of transportation along RA, from all the objections against the route RR, RB, and dividing by twice the cost of transportation per ton per mile on the connecting road.

The case may sometimes occur in which the dividing point will be found on the rival work instead of the connecting branch; but the proper modifications of the expression to render it applicable to this circumstance need not be particularly expressed.

SECTION VII.

OF THE MOST ADVANTAGEOUS CHARGES ON ARTI-
CLES OF SMALL VALUE.

40. Continuing to maintain the distinction previously established, between that portion of the trade of an improvement which will bear but a limited charge for transportation, and that which may become an object of competition, we will remark some important properties of each, which merit to be attentively observed.

If an uniform charge were adopted on the work, it is apparent that that portion of the products of the country which is situated nearest to their point of destination, would be capable of bearing the heaviest charge for carriage to or from the interior, before reaching, or after leaving, the line; and that, consequently, the tonnage proper to each unit of distance along the improvement near this point, would be greater than that belonging to the same space situated at more remote positions. This circumstance has been explained in a preceding section, where the base of the triangular space furnishing the trade, was shown to be nearest to the point to which the article would be forwarded; and this fact suggests immediately the propriety of so modifying the charge, as to levy at every point, the tax best proportioned to the ability of the trade to sustain.

To effect this object, we should abandon any scale approaching to uniformity, and adapt the prices at every important point, to the circumstances incident to the position.

Such a discrimination in the tariff of tolls is common on public works ; and the tendency of the practice is to promote the interest of the improvement, and is not irreconcilable with principles of justice.

41. I propose to show in what manner these prices should be regulated ; and for this purpose will represent by δ, the charge for *freight* per ton per mile on the work ; c the *toll*, and Π, h, &c., as in Section 5.

We shall then have for the greatest distance which the article will be carried into the interior after leaving the line, as before

$$\frac{\Pi - h\,\varsigma}{\beta} \; ;$$

and if we suppose the tonnage to be proportional to this distance, we shall obtain for its value

$$t\,\frac{\Pi - h\,\varsigma}{\beta} \; ;$$

where t represents the number of tons due to each mile along the lateral road.

If we multiply this quantity by c (the profit per ton

per mile), and observe to make $\mathfrak{c} = \delta + c$, we shall have for the revenue per mile due to this trade,

$$r = \frac{\Pi - h\,\delta - h\,c}{\beta}\; c. \qquad (7)$$

42. The most advantageous charge is that which will cause this revenue to be the greatest possible ; and to obtain it, we have only to determine the toll which will render the above equation a maximum.

Regarding c as variable, and differentiating this value of r, and drawing from it that value of c which satisfies the condition, we shall find

$$C = \frac{\Pi - h\,\delta}{2\,h}\; *, \qquad (8)$$

for the toll corresponding with the maximum revenue ; —*or the proper charge per ton per mile for toll, on articles which do not excite the competition of other lines, is equal to the difference between the whole charge which the article will bear, and the actual cost of transporting it on the improvement, divided*

---

* In the application of this equation for practical objects, we must observe to give to δ the value which it actually possesses under the circumstances. If the distance h is small, the cost of carriage will be greater—and it must always be adjusted in view of that circumstance.

by twice the distance it is carried on the improvement.

43. We will at once remark several important properties of this equation which should receive much attention in the selection of a system of internal improvement.

An article of value will bear a higher charge than one of less value, and consequently a long line designed for the conveyance of light and costly merchandise, may be constructed on a system of more expensive transportation, than one that is intended for cheap and heavy products.

At the same time, we will observe, it is an error to suppose that the most profitable part of the trade is that which is transported the greatest distance on the line. The supposition is sometimes correct; but the assertion cannot be advanced without qualifying the remark.

For that class of commodities for which there are other lines in competition, and which can sustain the charge of carriage to either, the difficulty of reaching the rival will increase, as we proceed along the improvement; and, consequently, the tax which we may impose on the trade will likewise increase.

But when that tax is limited by the nature of the article, and the cost of production, the conclusion will be directly the reverse. For such commodities, *not only the toll per ton per mile, but the aggregate toll for the whole distance the ton is carried, ought to be less when that distance is great, than when it is small.*

The reason appears in the above equation: the toll, or profit, must be half the charge which the commodity will yet bear, after the cost of freight is deducted from the charge which it would at first bear; and this remainder diminishes as the distance, in our progress along the line, increases.

It is important, therefore, for the success of the improvement, to tax highest the trade in the vicinity of its market—since it can always sustain a greater burthen than that which is more distant.

44. Another important result is the fact that *the higher the charge for freight on the line, the lower will be the toll ; the more expensive the system of transportation, the smaller will be the profit and the dividend.*

45. If to the foregoing value of the toll, equation (8), we add that of freight, we shall obtain for the whole tax, per ton per mile, when the charge is adjusted with a view to the maximum dividend,

$$\epsilon = \frac{\pi}{2h} + \frac{\delta}{2} ; \qquad (9)$$

an equation which teaches us that *the whole tax on the article will increase with every increase in the charge for freight ; while, at the same time, as we have seen, with every such increase the profit will be diminished ;* a fact which shows that the interests of the company who furnish the improvement, and of the public who supply the trade, as far as the consideration of charges is concerned, are here identical, and that both will be simultaneously subserved by the adoption of that system, for the long lines of this country, on which the freight is lowest.

46. We will recur to the fact demonstrated by equation (8)—the necessity of a diminution of toll for every increase of distance ; of charging high for the tonnage which is carried but a short space, and low for that which is transported further.

This is a principle resulting from the law of trade, which should not be disregarded in the establishment of the provisions of the charter of a company.   It ought to be an object of legislation, to cultivate the development of the internal resources of the common-wealth.   And to do this, the products of the interior must receive that aid from artificial means which nature has afforded to those on, or adjacent to, the ocean. The toll for the transportation of such objects should generally be reduced ; and a compensation should be sought in an increased tax on those which are more able to sustain it.

These limitations ought generally to be fixed by the charter, lest the future directors of the line be more disposed to proportion the charges to what they are authorized to exact, than to what the trade will bear, until experience shall have corrected the error.

47. For the purpose of applying the formula, let us suppose that the lumber on James river, intended for the Richmond market, would not bear a higher charge for transportation than four dollars per ton; and that they who are entrusted with the direction of the James River and Kanawha Company were about to establish the toll on that article, for all that would come on their line near Columbia, 60 miles above Richmond, and for that which they would receive in the neighborhood of Lynchburg, 90 miles higher up the river.

In these examples, their interest, according to the formula, would dictate for the proper charge, at Columbia,

$$C = 2 \tfrac{7}{10} \text{ cents per ton per mile};$$

and at Lynchburg,

$$C = 7 \text{ mills per ton per mile.}$$

We shall hereafter show cause why the true interest of the company would in all cases be promoted, by the reduction of these charges, further than would be authorized by the formula;* so that the proper and most judicious toll, in the case before us, would be, under the circumstances, about two cents at Columbia, and a half cent at Lynchburg.

Now, the company are confined by their charter to an uniform limit below the lower of these sums. I regard such a restriction on the trade of the eastern end of all the great lines of the country, as injurious to the works, without producing the effect contemplated by the

* Part ii. §5.

law. It prevents a company from deriving that profit from this portion of the trade of their line, which it could well afford to contribute, without proportionally cultivating the business which depends on the transportation of the article.

48. It is as far from my intention to object to the establishment of limits, for the purpose of protecting the community, as it would be to recommend to a company to pursue, without a liberal discrimination, that policy which would secure to them the greatest immediate pecuniary advantage.

I doubt not that restrictions are frequently necessary, to check the rapacity of corporate power; but believe that when they are imposed, the regulations should be made with proper regard to principle; that sufficient latitude should be given to them who are entrusted with the responsibility of governing the affairs of the institution, to discriminate, at least so far as to lay the heaviest burthen where there is the greatest ability to sustain. If this policy were pursued, the friends of such improvements might look upon the mineral products adjacent to the sea board, as a source of revenue to the stockholder, rather than as objects of embarrassment to the trade.

49. There is, on great works, which are prudently managed, but little danger of permanent extortion, however wide may be the latitude which is permitted. The fear of raising up a rival, the influence of an existing rival, or it may be, the interest which the proprietors of the

work feel in the advancement of the trade, will rarely be wanting in power sufficient for the protection of any interest.

And where all these might be inadequate, there would be a guarantee, in most instances, abundantly sufficient for the protection of the trade, in the law of the trade itself.

The Pennsylvania improvement, from Philadelphia to Pittsburg, is 396 miles long, and the freight may be fairly assumed at about $4\frac{1}{2}$ cents per ton per mile. Many of the most important articles forwarded from portions of that line, east of Pittsburg, would be incapable of sustaining a charge exceeding thirty dollars per ton.

With these data, equation (8) will give us

$$C = 1\frac{1}{2} \text{ cents per ton per mile.}$$

So that, without the co-operation of a rival, and supposing the navigation of the Mississippi to have no existence, and the mouth of that river to be closed against commerce, the state of Pennsylvania could not, with a consistent regard to the interest of the commonwealth, exact a higher toll on such articles, than one and a half cents per ton per mile.

These considerations, however, should not prevent the fixing of proper restrictions, in the establishment of a charter, for the protection of the commerce against the consequences of a tariff based on inadequate knowledge of the principles of trade.

50. By recurring to the preceding equations, we will

remark other properties that are worthy of observation. The toll corresponding with the maximum revenue compared with the expression given in Art. 33, shows us that *when the revenue is the greatest possible, the charge, or profit per ton per mile, is just half as great as that charge which would exclude the article from the line.*

It evidently follows from this fact, that, *when the revenue is greatest, the distance from which the commodity will be transported, or the tonnage of the improvement, will be just half as great as if the charge was only equal to the cost of carriage, and the revenue was consequently nothing.**

Another corollary of the same conclusion is, that, *when the dividend is the greatest possible, the profit derived from the commodity, on the improvement, is just equal to the extreme cost of transporting it to the line.*

51. These results are important in the administration of the affairs of an improvement, and in the preparation of the charter under which it is to operate.

Where the line is in the control of an incorporated company, the investigation teaches us, that however extortionate the views of its proprietors may be, they will never long attempt to levy a higher tax on their improve-

* The expression for the tonnage due to the toll which will produce the greatest revenue, is obviously the equation of a right line; and being of but half the value of that which is received when no toll at all is charged, the country supplying the trade may be represented by the lines Dn, Dn, (Fig. 3).

ment than the greatest sum paid by the article in reaching the improvement : and that where the work remains the property of a commonwealth, of which it may be the policy to increase the trade at the expense of revenue, there is a plain limit to the reduction that will be practised. For, when they have once attained the point at which the production of the work will be greatest, the effect of an utter sacrifice of the whole income of the improvement, on such articles, will be to increase the tonnage but one hundred per cent.

But that property of quantities susceptible of a maximum value, of changing but little when near the maximum, under a considerable modification of the variable, will always authorize a certain limited reduction of the toll, below the charge which would yield the greatest revenue ; and a corresponding augmentation of trade will result from the reduction. But beyond this limit, which we shall endeavor hereafter to establish,* any further reduction of the charge will be accompanied by a corresponding sacrifice of profit, which will rarely be compensated by the increased activity of trade, however highly its increase may be valued. And in this respect, there can be but slight difference between the true policy to be pursued in the government of the affairs of an improvement, whether immediate revenue, or tonnage, be the primary object.

52. If we substitute the value of ς given in equation

* See Part ii. § 5.

(9), in that of the tonnage, (Art. 41), we shall obtain for the tonnage due to the branch when the work is operating most profitably,

$$t \, \frac{\pi - h \, \delta}{2 \, \beta}. \qquad (10)$$

This trade is inversely as the charge for transportation on the tributary, and increases with any diminution of the charge for freight on the improvement.

53. Although these reflections are applied, in the investigation, only to those varieties of articles which are supposed to be uniformly distributed, it is not intended to admit that their applicability is limited to such.

Even for those isolated objects of commerce which are found in particular districts, of limited extent—as coal, and ores, and some other commodities—the toll may generally be more correctly established in the manner here indicated, than by any other means. The fact is still true, that the charge for conveyance on the line, which the commodity will bear, is limited; and consequently, the distance to which it will be carried abroad, the area of country that will be supplied, and the charge which should be levied on its transportation, are functions of the space through which it is moved, on the improvement.

They are, besides, functions of the same character as those which we have obtained above, and will generally lead to the same forms of expression for the results on the work.

SECTION VIII.

OF THE MOST ADVANTAGEOUS CHARGES ON ARTICLES
CONTENDED FOR BY RIVAL LINES.

54. In the establishment of a work of internal improvement, it will not be practicable to anticipate its effect on the commerce and trade of the country, and the reciprocal influence of this trade on the prosperity of the work, without due reference to existing and probable competitors. Not only the tonnage of the improvement, but the revenue of the work, and the most advantageous charge for toll are, for many objects of trade, dependant on the character of such rivals. In fact, it may be shown that the choice of a system, the cost of its construction, and, in many instances, the location of the line itself, are subject to their influence.

I propose to attempt an approximate solution of some of these points, as far as they depend on the consideration of the course of trade.

We have already seen that the tonnage which will be furnished to the improvement by any branch, or connecting road, is proportional to the distance along the road from which the commodity is brought to the line; and is represented by equation (6), the notation of which is explained in Art. 38.

The profit obtained by the company possessing the work, for the transportation of this trade over one mile of their improvement, is evidently equal to

$$\frac{X\beta + h'\varepsilon' - h\varepsilon + M}{2\beta}\, c ; \qquad (11)$$

and it is an object of the present inquiry to render this profit the greatest possible.

Differentiating the preceding expression with reference to c, and equating with zero, and observing to make $\varepsilon = \delta + c$, we shall find

$$C = \frac{X\beta + h'\varepsilon' - h\delta + M}{2h}, \qquad (12)$$

for the charge for toll which will give the greatest possible dividend on this division of the trade, coming from the branch in question.

We learn from the above equation that, when the markets offer equal attractions, *the toll corresponding with the maximum revenue is equal to the cost of sending the commodity from the point where it comes on the work to the rival port, less the cost of freight on the improvement, divided by twice the distance it is transported on the improvement.*

55. If to the above expression of the value of the toll, we add that of freight, we shall obtain

$$\delta + C = \frac{X\beta + h'\varepsilon' + h\delta + M}{2h}, \qquad (13)$$

for the whole charge on the article when the profits are greatest.

A comparison of these equations will teach us that, as in the other division of the trade, *any increase of the cost of freight will at the same time diminish the toll or profit on the article, and increase the whole tax upon it ;* and while the company suffer a loss of revenue, the public is taxed an additional amount for the transportation of its property.

56. By a further inspection of equation (12), we discover that the toll that ought to be levied, will increase as the distance increases between the rival market and the point where the road which brings the tonnage joins the line of the improvement, and as the whole cost of transporting the article from the junction to the rival market increases. It follows, therefore, that *if the trade under consideration be brought to the line by a common turnpike, a higher toll may be charged on it, than if it come by a rail-road, and, à fortiori, than if brought by a canal.*

We have an example in point, in the proposed turnpike or rail-road from the Tennessee and Virginia dividing line to Baltimore. Here the division of trade could be shown to be between Winchester and Buchanan, as assumed in the investigation ; and it is asserted, that the charge for the use of the James River and Kanawha improvement on all commodities belonging to the division under consideration, that would come by this route, ought to be higher if the branch were a common road than if it were a rail road, and higher if a rail road than if it were a canal—supposing the latter to be practicable.

The foregoing consideration ought frequently to have much weight in the selection of a system and the establishment of a line; and always in the arrangement of a tariff of toll.

57. If, in the general expression of the tonnage, equation (6), we make $x = 0$, and draw from it the value of ς under that condition, we will obtain the whole charge on the improvement, which will exclude the article entirely from the line, and force that portion of the commodity that is found in the district lying between the two works, to seek the rival market. By performing the operation, the equation yields

$$\varsigma = \frac{X\,\beta + h'\,\varsigma' + M}{h},$$

for the tax in question; and by observing that this charge is made up of the two quantities c and δ, we shall obtain for the value of the former, which will produce the same effect

$$c = \frac{X\,\beta + h'\,\varsigma' - h\,\delta + M}{h}; \qquad (14)$$

the toll which, if levied, would entirely shut out this branch of the trade.

58. The value of the toll obtained above, compared with that corresponding with the maximum dividend, shows us that the latter is just equal to one half the former ; or, in other words, *the profit per ton per mile, on this division of the trade, ought also to be equal to half the charge for toll which would exclude the commodity from the line.*

In this respect, the same law prevails in the trade in question, as in that of which the value is too low to justify competition ; and the fact stated above, may be regarded as general, under the condition of distribution of tonnage assumed in these pages.

A slight inspection of the formulæ which have led to this proposition, will again conduce to the other, equally apparent—that, *when the toll is the most advantageous, the distance from the improvement to the point where the trade begins to flow in the opposite direction, is half what would be the distance to the same point if no toll were charged.*

59. The foregoing conclusions appear, therefore, to be common to both divisions of the trade ; and the most advantageous charge, for any article, is half the charge which would exclude it from the work.

This fact, on a little reflection, will convince us of the importance to the community, as well as to the stockholders, of having the great lines of improvement in the country put under the control of the same interest. That is to say, it would result unfavorably to the public, as well as, generally, to one or other of the works, to have the trade carried a portion of the distance by one line, and then taken up, and transported the balance of the way by another.

It would be unfortunate, for instance, for the legislature of any state to give a charter to one company to construct an improvement from the Ohio to any point near tide, and to another, to extend the work to the navigation.

There are general inconveniences attached to such a system that must be obvious—but those to which I desire to limit my remarks, refer entirely to the trade, and toll and revenue.

Let us suppose such a line to be completed, and ready to go into operation ; and that the charge upon both divisions of it were made just sufficient to defray the cost of carriage. A certain balance, left from the whole tax which the article would bear, would then remain to be levied on for toll—and this balance is the sum that would, if exacted, exclude the trade from the line. If the proprietors of the longer of the two works were to establish their toll without reference to the other, they would appropriate the half of this balance for their profits, and leave the residue for the encouragement of the trade. If, then, the owners of the shorter line were to establish the tariff for their work, they would levy upon the half of this residue, and leave but the one fourth of the original tax in shape of toll, which the trade would bear, to go to the increase of the tonnage.

But the consequence of this would be, to cause the first company to reduce its toll down to one half the amount not taken by the second company, and thus give opportunity to the second, again to increase its exactions. And the ultimate result would be, if there were much disparity between the lengths of the lines, to cause two thirds of the whole toll which might be levied without excluding the trade, to be charged upon the two lines, and to leave but one third for the encouragement of the business.

This may be readily shown. For the purpose of the demonstration, we will call

P the greatest toll that could be exacted without entirely excluding the trade;

h the length of the longer of the two lines;

h' that of the shorter;

c the toll per ton per mile on the longer, and

c' that on the shorter.

Then the whole charge on the longer line, for a ton of merchandise carried the entire length of it, would be

$$h\,c\,;$$

and the charge which would afterward be exacted on the second line, would be

$$h'\,c' = \frac{P - h\,c}{2}\,.$$

But, at the same time, the toll that would be levied on the longer line must depend on that of the shorter, or will be represented by the equation,

$$h\,c = \frac{P - h'\,c'}{2}.$$

If we now eliminate $h'\,c'$ from these equations, we shall obtain the new condition,

$$h\,c = \frac{P}{3};$$

or the charge on the longer of the two lines will be just one third the charge for toll which would exclude the trade ; and by substituting this value of $h\,c$ in that of $h'\,c'$, we shall have for the latter quantity,

$$h'\,c' = \frac{P}{3};$$

and consequently, for the expression of the entire charge for toll that will be exacted,

$$h\,c + h'\,c' = \frac{2\,P}{3}.$$

60. It appears, then, that if there be no legal restriction imposed, it is in the ability of the directors of a short line coming between a great improvement and its market, to tax the trade just as much as it is taxed on the longer line. If the two parts of such an improvement

were of equal length, doubtless the administrators of the affairs of both would recognize a mutual benefit, in levying on many commodities precisely the aggregate toll that would be charged if the line were a continuous work in the control of one interest. But the disposition existing with each, to tax the trade at the expense of the other, would cause every commodity to be loaded with the greatest burthen it could bear, and not unfrequently with more than it would be the true interest of both to impose. And when the difference between the lengths of the lines is supposed to be great, the limit above stated will nearly, if not always, be obtained.

By dividing a line between two companies, without legal limitations to their charges, the toll or tax on the trade will be augmented one third, the profits of the longer improvement will be reduced, and the trade will of course suffer in proportion to the additional tax with which it is burthened.

Even the ordinary limitations prescribed by the charters of such companies, will not remove the entire objection to this practice. The tolls authorized by such acts are nearly always higher than it is the interest of a company possessing a work reaching far into the interior, to assess; and if the line were undivided, they would rarely approach those limits.

But in the case supposed, the shorter line would exercise the extent of its privilege, and to that extent would overburthen the trade, and impose on the greater work with which it is connected.

The same observation will apply to all the other charges to which the trade of the country is exposed in its passage through any line of improvement. At the points of transshipment and forwarding, in the application of power, or the supply of boats or cars,—if the service is performed by an association apart from that possessing the line, and having less interest in the promotion of the trade than the proprietors of the work,—unless it happen to be prevented by competition, a greater tax will be imposed on the trade, than it would be politic for the stockholders of the line to levy in performing the same service. And wherever the joint interest of all engaged in the same department of the business, amounts to less than the aggregate revenue of the work, competition itself does not offer a sufficient guarantee for the protection of the trade against the consequences of combinations among the competitors.

In general, therefore, it will be most expedient for the company possessing the improvement, to engage in whatever part of the business involves the necessity of imposing an additional tax on the trade. *They should permit no party to come between them and the public.*

In this respect, the system adopted by the state of Pennsylvania—of furnishing the improvement, and devolving on others the labor of the transportation—is impolitic. For, even if the commonwealth should perceive its interest in lowering the toll on any article, and accordingly reduce it, the very act would make it the interest of the independent carriers at once to increase their charge, and transfer the reduction of state toll to an augmentation of *their* toll.

There may be, in the general system adopted by Pennsylvania, inconveniences connected with the management of her complicated line in any other way, greater than this which she actually encounters, and that it is the selection she finds it best to make of the several evils.

This, however, is a question I do not mean to investigate. The case is only referred to as an important example pertinent to the subject before me.

61. In these, and all other observations in this volume, it is foreign from my design to discuss the political question, of the propriety of keeping the great lines of public improvements under the control of the state governments, or of turning them over to incorporated companies. My position in relation to one of those lines in this state, would probably deprive me of the character of a disinterested witness.

62. The tonnage drawn to the improvement under the charge which satisfies the condition of a maximum dividend, will be found by substituting the value of ξ given in equation (13), in the expression of the distance the article is carried to the work. The substitution being made, there results

$$t\,x = t\,\frac{X\,\beta + h'\,\epsilon' - h\,\delta + M}{4\,\beta},\qquad (15)$$

for the tonnage sought.

By inspecting the form of this equation, we will observe that when the value represented by

$$h'\,\epsilon' - h\,\delta + M$$

is negative, any increase of the cost of transportation on the connecting road will augment the tonnage of the improvement; and consequently, the trade furnished by the branch will increase with the increase of the whole cost of transportation towards the rival city, and with the increased charge per ton per mile on the line leading to it. So that, for all the trade to which the argument is intended to apply, it will militate to the advantage of the improvement, to have the cost of carriage on the lines leading from it to rival works, constructed in such manner that the cost of carriage may not be too low.

This conclusion may be easily misunderstood, if the train of the examination is not properly followed; and I will therefore add, that it is not intended to recommend that the proprietors of a central line should wish to see the cost of transportation generally increased on lateral roads leading to rival ports. Just the contrary. There are some articles on which the profit would be augmented by such an expedient; but there are at the same time others which could scarcely bear the previous charge, and might consequently be shut out entirely over certain districts by the increase, and deprived of the advantage of competition. Such articles would then be subject to the law which governs the trade designated, in the division here made, by that in articles of small value.

It is only when the condition expressed above has place, that an increase of tonnage would result from an increase of the charge for transportation on the connecting road. And this condition is equivalent to the assertion, that *when the distance from the improvement to the dividing point is less than one fourth the length of the connecting road, any increase of the cost of transportation on the connecting road will augment the tonnage received from that road ; and when this distance is greater than one fourth, any increase of freight on the tributary will diminish the tonnage derived from it.*

63. The fact that both the tonnage and the most advantageous charge for toll increase with the increase of distance between any improvement and its rival, is worthy of observation in a comparison of the isolated position of the James River and Kanawha improvement, with the proximity of the rival lines terminating at Pittsburg, and radiating from that city to the east.

SECTION IX.

OF THE MAXIMUM REVENUE.

64. It rarely happens, in the history of public works, that the revenue derived from an improvement is so

great, that it is not an object of solicitude with those entrusted with the administration of its affairs, to obtain
the means of augmenting it. Occasionally the circumstances may be such as to render the consideration of
revenue secondary to that of trade, and prompt to some
sacrifice of the former, for the sake of the latter ; but, in
general, after the reduction of the toll has reached a certain limit, the interests of the proprietors of the work,
and of them who supply the trade, will not be found to
be identical ; and it will require that every advantage be
taken of circumstances, of the position, necessities and
course of business, to obtain a moderate interest on the
investment. To arrive at this object most successfully,
is a part of the design of the foregoing researches; and
we are now in a condition to observe the measure of the
effect that may be produced.

65. The expression for the revenue derived from the
trade in articles of small value, coming to the line by
any branch, has been given in equation (7) ; and the
value of the charge for toll, which will render that quantity a maximum, was obtained in Art. 42, equation (8).

This latter charge, substituted in place of c in the
former expression, will give for the maximum revenue,

$$R = t \frac{(\Pi - h\,\delta)^2}{4\,\beta\,h} \qquad (16)$$

It appears from this equation, that *the maximum dividend per mile on this division of the trade will be*

*directly as the square of the difference between the
charge which the article will bear, and the whole cost
of freight on the improvement, and inversely as the
cost of carriage on the tributary which furnishes the
trade.*

66. A further inspection of equations (10) and (16),
shows the importance to the success of the work, of diminishing the distance along the improvement, from the
point of junction with the lateral road, to the terminus
of the line. In other words, it shows the propriety of
reducing the length of the line of the work to the utmost; since *the tonnage, the charge which may be levied
per ton per mile, and consequently the revenue, will all
receive an increase by a reduction of the length of transportation;* a consideration of the utmost importance in
the comparison of the rival works, seeking to draw the
trade of the western waters to the Atlantic.

67. The expression of the profit, or dividend per mile,
on all the trade brought by any branch communicating
with a competitor, has already been obtained, equation
(11); and the toll which would render the expression a
maximum, was produced in article 54, equation (12).

The value of the toll there found, being written in
place of c in equation (11), and the proper value being
given to ε, will produce, when multiplied by t,

$$R = t \frac{(X\beta + h'\varepsilon' - h\delta + M)^2}{8\beta h}, \qquad (17)$$

for the greatest possible dividend per mile, on the transportation of this division of the trade.

68. The same argument in favor of diminishing the length of the line, exists in this case, that we adverted to in the preceding; since we again observe, that the proper charge per ton per mile will increase with every diminution of distance; the expression of the tonnage will be similarly augmented, and the revenue per mile will receive a like and much greater addition.

The equation also teaches us that, if we consider the relative claims of the routes with reference to the point of junction of the tributary and the improvement, the revenue of the line derived from the trade of the tributary will be *directly as the square of the difference between the value of the objections* to the two routes, and inversely as the cost of transportation on that which leads to the rival port.*

69. It is sometimes popularly supposed, that although a change increasing the length of the line, may diminish the quantity of tonnage, there will be a compensation found in the fact, that the smaller quantity will pay toll for a greater distance of transportation. Though the argument is correct to a limited extent, the conclusion would be deceptive; and we will discover, in multiplying the charge C in equation (12), by the distance h, that the aggregate toll on one ton transported the whole length of the improvement, will, if the charges be judiciously ad-

* See Art. 38.

justed, be less on the longer, than on the shorter line; and by multiplying the expressions of the revenue, equations (16) and (17), by the same quantity, that the *aggregate dividend* will likewise be diminished by any such increase of distance.

It will be discovered, also, from equation (17), that the revenue will be increased by any increase of the distance, from the point where the tributary joins the work, to the rival improvement and the rival port.

70. These conclusions are of course built on the law of the distribution of tonnage which has been assumed, and presuppose a modification of the charges to correspond with the change of circumstances under which the operations are conducted.

But there are sometimes restrictions imposed, which prevent the fulfilment of such an intention, and interfere with the arrangements which would be made for the accomplishment of the object of obtaining, in every instance, the maximum of advantages.

The greatest toll which may be levied on any object, is usually established by law, and consequently the results of the calculation are not available beyond that limit.

If we suppose the values of C, in equations (8) and (12) to be, at the same time, the legal and most advantageous maxima, we obtain directly, for the points in the line at which we must cease, to apply this mode of regulating the toll,

$$h = \frac{\Pi}{2\,C + \delta} \text{ and } h = \frac{\Pi'}{2\,C + \delta} \, ;$$

where Π' is put for the sum of the cost of transporting the trade from the junction of the branch with the improvement to the rival port, and the value of the difference between the two markets.

SECTION X.

OF THE EFFECT OF LIMITATIONS OF THE CHARGES FOR TOLL.

71. The results obtained by the preceding examination are strictly to be relied on, when the conditions are such as supposed in the investigation. But, as was remarked in the last section, there are some qualifying circumstances which need to be regarded before it would be advisable to use the formulæ for general application.

We have hitherto supposed the charge for toll to be limited only by the capacity of the commodity to bear the tax, or by the competition tending to draw the trade in a different direction. The consequence of this basis, is to produce for the result a high tariff, near the point to which the trade is directed, and a more moderate toll on the tonnage which comes in at a greater distance. And if we apply the numbers which express the values of the toll represented in equations (8) and (12), for any of the common articles of commerce, we shall obtain, where the line is very short, a charge much exceeding what is usual on public works under similar conditions. The cause of this circumstance does not exist in any error of principle, but in limitations, fixed either by the charter of the corporation, or by the new competition which would be produced by an excessive imposition on the business of the country.

72. To illustrate this part of the subject by an example, we will suppose that there was a rail road from Scottsville, on James river, to Baltimore, and that the values of our notation become

$$X = 250 \text{ miles,} \qquad \beta = 4 \text{ cents,}$$
$$h = 80 \text{ miles,} \qquad \delta = 2 \text{ "}$$
$$h' = 0, \ \epsilon' = 0, \qquad M = -250;$$

conditions which imply that the value of freight from Scottsville to Richmond would be 2 cents per ton per mile, from Scottsville to Baltimore (including toll) 4 cents per ton per mile, and that the article would be worth $2 50 per ton, or 25 cents per barrel, on flour, more in Baltimore than in Richmond.

We shall then have, by equation (12),

$$C = 3\tfrac{11}{16} \text{ cents per ton per mile,}$$

for the toll which would yield the greatest profit on the trade of that branch.

But the company are limited, by their charter, to a toll of about two cents per ton per mile, on such commodities as they may anticipate from this source.

It follows, consequently, that the formulæ are not applicable, under these conditions, for most articles of trade on the James River and Kanawha improvement, until we ascend to a higher point than Scottsville on the line.

73. Let us next suppose that there would be no rail road from Scottsville ; but, instead, one from the mouth of the North Branch to Baltimore, and that the values of the symbols in the formula were $X = 252$ miles, $h = 175$ miles, $h' = 0$, $\varepsilon' = 0$, $\beta = 4$ cents, $\delta = 1\frac{1}{4}$ cents, $M = -250$.

In this case, we shall have for the toll that ought to be charged,

$$C = 1\tfrac{1}{2} \text{ cents per ton per mile.}$$

It appears, then, that at the mouth of the North river, and west of it, the company would have it in their power to charge a much higher toll, than it will eventually be found to be their true interest to exact. We may therefore apply the principles of the investigation with security to both divisions of the trade, derived from the country beyond the Blue Ridge. East of that line, the limitations prescribed by the charter will generally limit their applicability to the heavy articles of small value for which there is no competition.

74. But even without legislative enactments to protect the trade from extortionate charges, there would still be a control over the company, exercised by the common roads parallel with it, and the danger of other more serious rivals, for that part of the trade of which the situation would suffer it to be overburthened.

The restrictions imposed by these causes, give rise to certain qualifications of the results previously announced, which it will be our object to point out.

75. The general expression of the value of the revenue per mile, for the trade which is an object of competition, is given in equation (11).

If, in that expression, we make ς represent the limit of the aggregate charge, and c the limit of the toll per ton per mile, which may be levied on the commodity, whether it be the consequence of legislative interference, or of any other influence, we shall have the value of the revenue under this new condition. The equation which represents it, may be then put under the form

$$t \frac{\pi' - h\,\varsigma}{2\,\beta}\,c\,;$$

in which shape it resembles the expression, (Art. 41.)

$$t \frac{\pi - h\,\varsigma}{\beta}\,c,$$

of the revenue per mile on those articles which will bear but a low tax for transportation, and are not sought for in the competition offered by other lines.

76. An inspection of either of these forms will satisfy us, that when these limits for the charges are adopted, the revenue per mile derived from the commodities brought to the line by similar branches, will diminish as the length of the line, or the distance from the outlet of the

work to the branch increases. A palpable consequence of this conclusion is, that *if all other things are equal, and the cost per mile of two lines of unequal length, between the same points, is the same, the greater dividend will always be obtained from the shorter.*

77. There is, however, another question connected with this subject, likely to arise in the establishment of the location of works of internal improvement, which merits a passing consideration.

It sometimes happens that there is a choice of routes, and that the aggregate cost of the shorter, is greater than that of the longer; and the preceding section has shown, that in all such cases it will be the true policy of the engineer to adopt the shorter, if the toll which the company shall exact is at their discretion, provided the difference in cost do not exceed a certain limit, which we shall hereafter determine.

But in consequence of the restrictions under which the act of incorporation usually constrains a company to operate, such a policy might become questionable; for we will perceive, by multiplying the preceding equations by h, the length of the line, that the expression of the aggregate revenue will be, for the trade in objects of small value,

$$t \; \frac{\Pi - h\,\mathfrak{e}}{\beta} \; h \, c; \qquad (18)$$

and for that liable to be subjected to the competition of
rival improvements

$$t \, \frac{\Pi' - h \, \varepsilon}{2 \, \beta} \, h \, c \, ; \qquad (19)$$

quantities obviously susceptible of maxima with reference to the distance h.

Making h variable, and differentiating, and equating
with zero, as required by the rules for such cases, we
shall obtain from these equations,

$$h = \frac{\Pi}{2 \, \varepsilon}, \qquad 20)$$

for the length of the line which would produce the greatest aggregate revenue for that division of the trade for
which there is no competition ; and

$$h = \frac{\Pi'}{2 \, \varepsilon}, \qquad (21)$$

for the division which is sought for by rival improvements.

78. These results are important, in many respects, in
the location of an improvement; for they show us that,
although for all more distant trade than is represented
by the foregoing values of h, it will be proper to reduce
the length of the line, yet for that within this limit, it
will be best to increase it up to the limit. That is to
say, that if a choice of routes should occur, of which

one was longer than the other, but similar in all other respects, it would be better, for the trade due to points near the sea-board, that the longer route should be adopted, if the length of the longer be not greater than

$$\frac{\Pi}{2\,\epsilon}, \quad \text{or} \quad \frac{\Pi'}{2\,\epsilon}.$$

But it must be recollected that, generally, this consideration applies to a very small portion of the trade, while it is essential that, for all the more distant transportation, the length of the line should be diminished. It does not follow, therefore, that it would be proper to make choice of the longest line within the limits designated, but merely that it would be worth more to diminish the length beyond that limit than within it.

79. The investigation will teach us that a discrimination ought to be made between the principles which should govern the location of any line, of greater length than the values of h, in equations (20) and (21), and that of its tributaries. The branches are not affected by the more distant trade; and consequently, if the whole length of the line, from the origin of the improvement to the termination of the branch, be less than $\frac{\Pi}{2\,\epsilon}$ and $\frac{\Pi'}{2\,\epsilon}$, it will be proper, wherever a choice of routes occurs on the branch, to select the longer, if it be equally favorable in other aspects.

80. To increase the length of the line may sometimes be an object of importance to the stockholders, when their improvement is the extension of any other work stretching into the interior, and bringing a distant trade upon it. And it is in this case, that the subject before us possesses the greatest importance. Here it might be their interest, (if they were disposed to violate those principles of good faith, which the commonwealth, in granting a charter, has a right to anticipate), to tax the trade by forcing it to traverse a longer line than needful, and in that way compensate, somewhat, for the restrictions placed upon the charges which they are permitted to assess. This consideration may be regarded as an additional objection to the policy before adverted to, of dividing an improvement between two companies, even where restrictions are imposed.

In all such cases, the most profitable length of line for articles of heavy burthen, and small value, will be *half the charge which the article will bear, divided by the limit of the tax per mile upon its transportation;* and for those commodities which must be obtained under a competition with another work, *half the cost of sending the article from the junction of the branch to the rival port, added to half the value of the superiority of the mart on the line over that of its rival, and divided by the limit of the whole charge per ton per mile, which the company is permitted to levy.*

81. On closing this division of our subject, it may be

observed, that there are many important views connected with the object of the inquiry, which it has not been thought expedient to introduce. The course of the investigation has indicated the method proper to be adopted, for the most prominent examples incident to the practice of the engineer; the modifications which will be rendered necessary by the peculiarities of particular cases, will sometimes demand examinations made expressly for the object. It is believed, however, that all the most important of these that will occur, may be brought under some one of the heads already discussed.

I may add, that it is not always indispensable to establish the toll for every point, and for each article, by means of a rigid adherence to the formulæ, for the commodity and position. For every line, a general scale of charges may be constructed, which will approach near enough to the object to satisfy the conditions of the problem, and produce a salutary influence on the result, and yet avoid discriminations that would be regarded as invidious.

PART II.

TRADE OF THE OHIO AND MISSISSIPPI.

———

SECTION I.

PROBABILITY OF THE WORKS IN PROGRESS BETWEEN
THE ATLANTIC AND WESTERN WATERS, BEING
FOUND ADEQUATE TO THE ACCOMMODATION OF THE
PROSPECTIVE TRADE.

82. In discussing the relative merits of the several lines
of communication between the Atlantic and the west, and
the value of their respective pretensions to the command
of the trade, it is proper that we should be able to form
some estimate of the probable importance of the trade
itself. Accuracy, or any thing approaching to accuracy,
is not to be looked for in an anticipation of the possible
destiny of a region, which is yet hardly in a state of transi-
tion from the condition of a wilderness to that of ordinary
cultivation.

The sources of the principal rivers which flow into
the Mississippi, have scarcely been reached by the hunter,

and none but the richest and most favored spots have arrested the progress of the emigrant. The great territory watered by these streams, is, in fact, but beginning to be settled; the wants of the population are few, and society is so little advanced, that the country is but commencing to throw off a surplus of production.

It is natural that a mind familiar with the extent and fertility of this territory, should form exalted opinions of the probable results of time and enterprise applied to a field so favorable; and that, sometimes, sooner than attempt to estimate things so vast, should set them down as almost inestimable.

Indeed, looking upon the influence which even these sparse settlements upon the borders of the streams that spread over the west, have had on the commerce of the country; the crowds of boats that are kept in activity from Pittsburg and St. Louis, to the Gulf of Mexico; the city which has been created at the point of meeting of these products and the shipping,—it is not surprising that, in attempting to fill up the vacant space of the west,— to imagine the prairies tilled, and the wilderness peopled, and the villages converted into cities,—the most temperate mind should conceive a picture apparently too boundless for an estimate of its extent.

83. Nor ought we to be surprised that the enthusiastic patrons of the great lines of internal improvement, should, in the fervor of their zealous advocacy of the projects which have commanded their patronage, look forward to

the day when the progress of the west in strength and improvement, may prove the inadequacy of all the artificial channels which are in progress to supply its demands, and to vent the produce which it will throw off to supply the wants of other people. At the same time, we have a glimmer of the light of experience in the result of the improvements of Pennsylvania, which would seem to countenance the incredulity of them who deny the ability of such works to enter at all effectually into competition with steam on the Ohio and Mississippi; since that work is thought yet to have exercised but a limited influence in changing the direction of the trade for any considerable distance below its western terminus.

Several questions, therefore, naturally arise in this condition of things, which are deeply interesting to the proprietors of the works in question, and to the states through which they are constructed.

84. It is important to determine whether the direction of the trade can be changed entirely, or whether the freights of these improvements will not be limited to certain descriptions of merchandise of moderate extent; and if so, whether its division among so many candidates will not render the competition ruinous to all.

I do not despair of proving, in the following pages, the ability of these improvements to change the direction of trade on articles of every description, which are forwarded from or to the valley of the Mississippi; but I propose now to test the ability of the works to give passage to this tide of productions, in the event of their offering inducements for its transmission.

85. It is not unusual for the warm advocates of particular improvements, when discussing the comparative advantages of the several lines aiming for the western trade, to console themselves with the reflection that, although their favorite scheme may not be the most favored by circumstances, yet the quantity of products to be discharged, will necessarily throw as much in its way, as it will be able to receive.

To make an approximate conjecture of the correctness of such a conclusion, we may attempt to estimate the probable future trade of the Mississippi valley.

But a small portion of the country using this river, below the mouth of the Ohio, can ever be closely connected in commerce with the ports on the Atlantic. If the improvements which are laid across the Alleghany, can turn the trade of the Missouri and its tributaries up the Ohio, and command that of the latter stream, it may be regarded as the limit of their capacity. They would then drain of its produce, and supply with its groceries and merchandise, a region of more than one million of square miles, and which excels the sea-board states in productiveness. We shall limit the discussion therefore to the trade of the Missouri and the Mississippi, above the mouth of the Ohio.

86. It is not assuming too much to say, that the country, watered by the Mississippi and its branches, is

destined, in a very moderate space of time, to rival the present average condition of New York or Pennsylvania, in the denseness of its population, and in the trade which springs from their exertions. Indeed, if we form our conclusions from the data furnished by the western states, we shall be forced to admit, that it will probably not exceed forty years before this million of square miles will number twenty millions of inhabitants; and will send abroad from an area, twenty times greater than that of New York, at least an amount of productions, when compared with the latter, proportionate to their respective population.

87. Let them who question the correctness of this supposition, but look at the statistics of any of the middle and western states; and remark an increase of more than two millions, in forty years, for New York; of more than a million for Ohio; and note the rapidity of the progress of those states, which have only begun to come into notice since the last census.

Let them but reflect, for a moment, on the changes which have been effected on the waters of the west, in the memory of those who are still young; consider that this country presents an almost boundless field for the development of enterprise, and a charm for all who are prepared to barter indolence at home, for the reward of privations in the west.

There is scarcely a man now engaged in the active pursuits of business, who cannot recollect when the first boat essayed its first venture on the waters of the Ohio and Mississippi; and the commerce of those streams now keeps in activity a fleet of nearly four hundred steam vessels.

88. But admitting my postulate to be correct, and that in forty years the inhabitants of this portion of the Mississippi valley will number twenty millions, and the tonnage which they will send off for the support of the works leading to the Atlantic, will be proportional to that which is furnished by the population of the state of New York, to the works of that commonwealth, we will obtain by a reference to the tonnage of the canals of that state,* exclusively of the products of the forest, about six millions of tons, for the annual aggregate demand and supply of the valley of the Mississippi.

If we suppose that this tonnage will be all taken across the Alleghany on canal boats, or in trains of cars, of which each boat or train will carry one hundred tons, we will have the aggregate number of 60,000 trips per annum, or 164 boat loads per diem; or, allowlowing for the irregularity of trade, we may safely say, 240 boat loads, or trains each day.

---

* A report of the canal commissioners of New York, for 1837, gives for the aggregate tonnage for all the state canals for 1836, one million three hundred and ten thousand eight hundred and thirty-six tons; of which seven hundred and fifty-five thousand two hundred and fifty-two tons was produce of the forest.

These data will give us about 10 boat loads per hour, for a work which might be kept in operation during the whole year.

89. In estimating the capacity of an improvement for the accommodation of a portion of this trade, we are not to take for its measure the actual performance on any of the lines in the country. An increase of business will give rise to improvements in the system, adequate to its wants; and we must not consider a canal liable to breaches, with single locks, and of imperfect construction; nor a rail road with an insecure foundation, liable to derangement from frost, and to obstruction from slides, and traversed by locomotives equally inadequate, as the means that would be provided, to give passage to the whole trade of a continent. When the business created by a population of many millions has to be transacted along a line of canal or rail road, every resource that can be obtained from the increasing application of science and art, will be brought in requisition. The canal will be provided with an additional towing path, and as many locks as are necessary; the valves will be adjusted to the time of filling essential to the purpose; the banks will be strengthened until breaches are impossible, and protected against the waves by an indestructible material; the mountain streams will be passed under, and the washings of every acre will be discharged through adequate openings: the rail roads will be still more improved; their foundations will be more permanent, their

rails will be more substantial, the drainage will be perfect; the weights of the engines will be increased, the cars made more convenient, and the trains, if necessary, will be driven by a power adequate to the management of a thousand tons.

Under such circumstances, the transshipments will take place at points where the population of great cities may engage in the shifting of the produce from the boats to the cars, and from the cars to the boats. The lines will terminate where they can approach the shipping, and the trade at the port need only be limited by the capacity of the improvement.

90. Then, what portion of this trade of the west can any one work hope to be able to accommodate? Regarding only the power of the system, and supposing it to be under an efficient and energetic administration, I have no hesitation in saying, that the whole business which would be created by this population of 20,000,000 of inhabitants, could be passed over any one of the lines, properly improved, which are now in competition from the Lakes and the Ohio, to the Atlantic. I have no scruple in pronouncing, that a much more important trade than would be conducted by these ten boats (or five in each direction) per hour, may be passed, under proper management, and with the resources of modern art, through all the locks and over all the grades of any line which is now in course of construction across the Alleghany.

91. If, then, we reflect that there are even now, before this trade has fairly commenced to flow, eight lines constructed, or in progress between the St. Lawrence and the Mississippi, besides the Mississippi itself; and others suggested, which will eventually be put under way, we must admit, that in the next few centuries there will hardly be as much business as they can all perform.

An immense amount of produce must ever continue to pass to the ocean by the Mississippi, and new rivals must be looked for in other quarters.

The rough calculation that is here offered, is predicated on the supposition that a population will have taken possession of the country drained by all the tributaries of the Mississippi and Missouri; but when that event will have taken place, we cannot assume that the wide territory west of the Rocky Mountains will remain quite unpeopled. Settlements will there also have swelled into states, and villages into cities; and in all probability, the adventurer who now finds it practicable only to obtain his supplies from the occasional steamboat that ascends the Yellow Stone, will then have an outlet by the Colorado or Oregon.

92. But looking only to the present lines, we perceive the almost hopeless chance, that the capacity of any one of the contemplated improvements will ever be fully tested.

The Mississippi will remain a permanent and controlling rival, which will forever invite a portion of the business to seek the Gulf of Mexico; and the means

that are now in progress, and that will hereafter be im-
measurably increased, to draw it by the way of the
Lakes to the St. Lawrence, and by the Erie canal to
New York, must leave the possessors of the improvements
terminating on the Ohio, in the necessity of exercising
their best skill and management to preserve their trade.

93. My object in attempting to demonstrate this fact,
is to show that a spirit of competition is likely to prevail
for all time between these several routes to the west ; that
they are competitors for the same prize, and that whatever is gained by the one, will be lost by the other. I
by no means doubt the adequacy of the trade of the west
eventually to sustain them all, and justify their construction by the richest reward of the enterprise of their
projectors. Indeed, I by no means doubt that each and
all of these lines, if well conducted, will amply remunerate their proprietors, the moment that they are open
to the west ; and that the business that would be done
on more than one of them, would be sufficient to dis-
charge the interest on the capital expended in their construction, if it should so happen that they could not
receive one ton of produce from, or send one ton of
goods into the valley of the Ohio.

The travel which will take place, and the domestic
trade which will be developed, on the route of the improvements, would alone be sufficient to sustain them.
The Erie canal is a magnificent example of such a
result ; the Pennsylvania improvement, it is to be hoped,

will eventually be another; and I will not hesitate to associate with them the James and Kanawha line, and perhaps, in this particular, the New York and Erie rail road.

94. But notwithstanding this fact, I think it is clear, that no one of the routes in question will ever receive all the tonnage that might be transported over it; and that the trade that will exist when the productiveness of the west has attained its utmost limit, will be an object for the emulation of anxious competitors which can never be fully satisfied.

In this view of the subject, it is important that we glance again at the positions of this trade, and of the lines which are contending for its possession.

95. The greater share of the trade of the Lakes— comprehending the southern borders of Canada, and the northern parts of Illinois, Indiana, Ohio and nearly the whole of Michigan—and, in all probability, at some future, and not very distant day, that of a considerable extent of the country west of Lake Michigan, has passed, beyond redemption, to New York. Her Erie canal, in its present imperfect form, commands it, and the enlarged work which will take its place as the former disappears, will probably secure it forever. Her Erie rail road will be adequate to its partial preservation, when the cold of winter renders the former work, and its competitor of Pennsylvania, inoperative. There is no ground for a rival for

this trade south of Canada, where a successful competition with New York is hardly likely to be maintained.

But another condition of things exists as we fall back on the tributaries of the Ohio, and seek there the chances of the competition.

96. The direction of this river, on the west of Pennsylvania, Maryland and Virginia, is nearly parallel with the line connecting the cities of Philadelphia, Baltimore, Washington and Richmond, where the works of those states would respectively connect with tide-water. But after passing the central part of Virginia, its direction is nearly due west, while that of the coast is not materially changed.

The consequence of these peculiarities of the geography of the country is, that the lines of the abovenamed states will not differ widely in length, while that of any southern competitor aiming to intercept the trade, must run nearly parallel with the river, for whatever distance the length of its line exceeds those of the others, and encounter, in that distance, a competition with the facilities afforded by the western steamboats.

97. General as these facts are, I consider them sufficiently definite to show at once, that the rivalry that has place, must be chiefly limited to the space between the mouth of the Kanawha and the city of Pittsburg.

In this space there are five competitors among which the trade is to be divided ; and of these five, four of the termini are concentrated in a distance of 70 miles from the junction of the Alleghany and Monongahela; and the fifth—the James River and Kanawha improvement— opens upon the Ohio at a point 260 miles below that place.

This latter work will have, then, the advantage due to the navigation of 260 miles of the river, where that navigation is most imperfect; the additional advantages of a milder climate, and the monopoly of her own domestic trade over a wider area east of the Ohio, than can be enjoyed by the other works, which radiate from the same point.

Opposed to these advantages is the present superiority of capital, and the enterprise consequent upon its possession, in the larger cities with which it is to cope.

98. To decide between the relative claims of these candidates for the Ohio trade, we must have regard to the principles by which it will be governed; the further elucidation of which, is the subject about to occupy our attention. It is not, however, my design to apply those principles for the purpose of invidious comparison.

That there will always be a warm competition for the trade, is not to be doubted; since it has already been shown, that in the next half century it cannot amount to more than will be abundantly accommodated by one well constructed and well managed improvement; and it is my object to show, in general, what considerations should govern the location and conduct of all these improvements, to render their success most certain.

What the present value of this trade may be, is difficult to determine with the accuracy that is desirable. The best information I can obtain on the subject, would show that the whole of the present trade of the western waters, (exclusive of lumber), is but about half as great as the present tonnage on the eastern end of the Erie canal. I estimate it from 400,000 to 500,000 * tons per annum. The latter quantity may be rather too high—but if so, it will perhaps be low enough by the time the estimate is printed. In the particular applications which I shall have occasion to make, however, the smaller number will be used.

SECTION II.

OF THE TRADE OF THE WEST, FOR WHICH STEAM-
BOATS ON THE OHIO AND MISSISSIPPI ARE COMPE-
TITORS.

99. The subject which it is proposed now to take up, brings us at once to the arena upon which the great improvements of the country are the competitors, and the produce of many millions of acres, poured into the no-

---

* This paragraph was written in the month of April. Since the volume was put in the hands of the printer, I have received the New Orleans price current for Oct. 1st., which, together

blest rivers of the world by a thousand tributaries, is the prize. This vast trade is conducted by about four hundred steamboats, which circulate from the Gulf of Mexico, more than 2,000 miles, by the Ohio and its branches, in one direction, and a much greater distance by the Mississippi and Missouri, in another. It is increasing, too, with a rapidity nearly commensurate with the means that are in preparation to carry it off, and is consequently still offering new allurements to the enterprise of the candidates for its possession. And every year's experience, consequently gives additional interest to the question of the best mode of changing the direction of this tide of commerce—which s now carried down these rivers, and constitutes the wealth of New Orleans,—and making it contribute to the advancement of the seaboard states.

And, it must be admitted, that it is an object not unworthy of science, and the application of professional skill, to find a mode that is adequate to the lifting of the products of an almost boundless region, from the rivers into which they are poured, elevating them to the summit of one of the loftiest chains of mountains on the

with other facts in my possession, offers sufficient evidence, that it would not be estimating the trade too high to consider 500,000 tons its value for the present year. (See Appendix.)

In this estimate, it is not intended to embrace the trade between different parts of the valley. It refers only to the exports and imports of the west,—to the produce and manufactured articles sent abroad, and the importations received from abroad.

continent, and delivering them into the vessels which are waiting to bear them to another hemisphere.

100. It is proposed now to ascertain the laws of this trade, and also learn to what extent the transportation on the lines between the Ohio and the Atlantic is controlled by the competition offered by the steamboats on the western waters.   And in attempting to reduce the subject to the order necessary for the application of rules which depend on rigid principles of analysis, I do not profess to hope to remove all objections to the system which I am compelled to adopt ; but I trust that the method will be sufficiently approved to produce all desirable confidence in the results.   Certainly, we are more likely to arrive at correct general conclusions, by a faithful examination of the question on an hypothesis liable to some objections, than if we take to the unlimited field of conjecture.

101. The question immediately before us, is that of the trade which is to be obtained by drawing it away from New Orleans, where it would be sent, but for the influence of the improvement. But many of the objects of commerce, found below any given point on the river, are also to be met with, to some extent, above it; and if the mouth of the Kanawha be selected as the point towards which the produce from either direction is attracted, it is evident that a solution of the question embracing the whole ground, would not permit us to waive the consideration of that portion of the business which belongs to the river above that point.   But, if the influence of the James River and

Kanawha improvement prove sufficient to draw any article up the Ohio and forward it to Richmond, it is evident
that the same article would not, in descending, pass by
that line ; and that if there were no northern outlet to
the up-river trade, it must of necessity likewise be arrested
at Point Pleasant, and drawn to Richmond.

But as there is actually a rival work from Philadelphia and Pittsburg, a new question will arise ; and it
will become important to know, not only what influence
this competitor may exercise on the trade between Point
Pleasant and Pittsburg, but also its probable effect on the
trade below Point Pleasant.

Before engaging in the consideration of this general
question, we will take the more limited case of one of
these routes contending with the city of New Orleans,
for that portion of the trade which is found below the
embouchure of the work.

102. The principle of the investigation is precisely
the same as we have hitherto adopted ; and we shall
consider, that the direction of the trade will depend on
the joint influence of the cost of transportation, and the
choice of markets. For various reasons, it will be more
convenient to deduce the equations again, than apply
those which we have already obtained ; and for this
object we will designate by

X the distance from the improvement to New Orleans by the river ;

x the distance from the improvement to the point where the trade is divided;

h the length of the line of improvement;

c the charge por ton per mile, for toll;

δ the cost per ton per mile, of freight;

$c + \delta = \mathfrak{E}$, the whole charge per ton per mile on the improvement;

π the freight per ton per mile on the Ohio and Mississippi rivers; and

M the difference between the values of the market at New Orleans, and that at the eastern end of the improvement.

103. In determining the point of division, and other circumstances of the trade, it is necessary to know the character of the last of the above quantities; and for the sake of simplicity, we shall uniformly regard it as favoring the Atlantic ports.

There is, withal, no doubt that these would generally be preferred. The merchant on the Ohio and Mississippi would rather pay an additional sum for the transportation of his goods, and purchase them in New York or Philadelphia, than obtain them cheaper by the way of New Orleans. The manufacturer of flour on the Scioto or Muskingum, would prefer to send the product of his mill to Richmond, and pay an additional tax for conveyance, to the risk of detention, and possible damage, in a southern climate.

There are various circumstances which tend to give the eastern ports a preference, and the dealer in the commodity always knows at what he values that preference: the transporter may, by an attention to the details of his business, soon learn it.

104. To examine the question—we have

$$(X - x)\,\pi$$

for the freight, from the dividing point to New Orleans; and for the charge on the commodity, from the same point to the Atlantic port,

$$h\,\mathfrak{E} + x\,\pi\,;$$

and the difference between these two quantities, ought to be equal to the difference between the advantages of the rival markets. We have therefore the equation

$$h\,\mathfrak{E} + x\,\pi - (X - x)\,\pi = M,$$

from whence we obtain directly,

$$x = \frac{X\,\pi - h\,\mathfrak{E} + M}{2\,\pi}\,;\qquad(22)$$

for the distance down the Ohio, below the outlet of the work, to the point from which the trade would begin to be attracted to the improvement. This distance, by the conditions of the problem, is proportional to the trade which it furnishes.*

* The tonnage obtained from each mile of the Ohio, is in fact a function of the charge on the improvement; for as soon as we reach a point in the valley, where the work offers greater attraction to the trade than the descending navigation, it is

105. We can perceive several facts, of some import-ance, which are demonstrated by this equation.

If we draw from it the value of ς which renders $x = 0$, we shall have the charge upon the improvement which will exclude the trade from the line. This charge is

$$\varsigma = \frac{X \pi + M}{h};\qquad (23)$$

and the tax, in shape of toll, which will produce the same result, is as obviously

$$c = \frac{X \pi - h \delta + M}{h}.\qquad (24)$$

106. We may apply this formula to the James and Kanawha improvement, and ascertain what the future charges must be, on the western trade, to enable that work to enter into competition with the river navigation.

I have elsewhere stated, that this line will be about

obvious that any reduction of the charges on the improvement, will draw produce to the river from more distant points in the interior. It may, however, be readily shown, that the probable fluctuations of the toll will have no sensible effect on the coeffi-cient of the tonnage, and not sufficient influence on any ques-tion to render it expedient to embarrass the solution by an attempt to allow for this consideration.

We should, nevertheless, be so far mindful of the circum-stance, as to regard it as an additional reason, to make the tariff always rather lower than the following investigation will indicate to be the proper charge.

465 miles long; that it terminates on the Ohio, at the mouth of the Great Kanawha, about 1740 miles above New Orleans, and that the future average charge for freight will not exceed $1\frac{7}{10}$ cents per ton per mile, over the whole line. (See Appendix).

The quantity representing the difference between the advantages of the markets has no general value, and should, therefore, only be employed in particular cases where it is previously ascertained.

With these data we have

$$X = 1740 \text{ miles}, \quad \pi = \tfrac{3}{4} \text{ cent},$$
$$h = 465 \text{ miles}, \quad \delta = 1\tfrac{7}{10} \text{ cents}, \ M = 0 ;$$

and consequently, by equation (24),

$$c = 1\tfrac{1}{10} \text{ cents per ton per mile.}$$

Or, *it is certain that, in general, the James River and Kanawha Company can charge not more than one cent and one mill per ton per mile on any article which will not command a higher price at Richmond than at New Orleans;* and that if their tariff be higher, the commodity will be wholly excluded from the line, and forced to seek some other channel.

107. It is frequently convenient to know, what is a safe sum to assume for the average superiority of the eastern markets, for some of the most important articles of western growth. We have not yet sufficient facts to fix such a mean value from the experience of the country; but the occasional results on the Pennsylvania im-

ments, will furnish us with useful examples for the purpose of illustration.

By drawing the value of M from equation (22), we shall find

$$M = (2\,x - X)\,\pi + h\,\mathfrak{E}\,; \qquad (25)$$

a convenient expression for the object in question.

To apply this formula, we know that when the Ohio is in navigable condition, and the line is open, bacon and tobacco are carried in considerable quantities from Pittsburg to Philadelphia, a distance of 396 miles, at the rate of $87\frac{1}{2}$ cents per 100 lbs., or $4\frac{95}{100}$ cents per ton per mile : that the same articles are frequently brought up the river from Cincinnati and Louisville, and sometimes even a greater distance, to take that route. The length of the water course, from Pittsburg to New Orleans, may be called 2000 miles ; and the distance which these, and some other articles, are carried to the improvement, may be safely assumed at 600 miles. We have, then, for the values of the characters in the equation, $X = 2000$ miles, $x = 600$ miles, $h = 396$ miles ; $\pi = \frac{3}{4}$ cents, $\mathfrak{E} = 4\frac{95}{100}$ cents ; and consequently,

$$M = \$13\ 60,$$

for the value, under these circumstances, of the superiority of the Philadelphia market, over that of New Orleans, for the heavy products of the west.

108. It may be remarked that, for the commodities named, this estimate is sometimes much too low ; and

that for cotton, the true value is at least 50 per cent. higher than that here given.

For flour, and a great variety of other articles, it is something less; though the fluctuations are perhaps greater in flour, than in the other objects of trade which are here designated. If we call the difference on this article $8 it will not vary materially from the mean value it possesses.

109. Now, it will be a question of some interest to know the greatest charge for toll which may be levied on the James River and Kanawha improvement, without so far over-burthening the trade, as to exclude it entirely from the line—taking into consideration, the influence of the superiority which the eastern marts possess over that of New Orleans.

And for this purpose, I imagine, we may anticipate that the Richmond market will have an advantage of at least $10, per ton, on those commodities for which that of Philadelphia is generally from thirteen to fifteen dollars.

Employing this value in equation (24), we shall have

$$c = 3\tfrac{1}{4} \text{ cents ;}$$

or, the charge which would exclude the commodity from market, would be, on the James River and Kanawha improvement, 3 cents and $2\tfrac{1}{2}$ mills per ton per mile, exclusive of the charge for freight. This may be regarded as near the maximum toll which it would be in the power of the company to levy, if the charter gave them full power over the subject, and there were no check presented by any rival improvement on the north.

110. If we now insert this value of M in equation (22), and apply it again to the James River and Kanawha improvement, (making $\mathcal{6} = 1.7$) we shall be able to anticipate the portion of the valley of the Ohio, of which the trade may be drawn to Richmond, by sacrificing all the profits of the work to the purpose of obtaining it. The substitution being made, we have

$$x = 1010 \text{ miles.}$$

Or, if the charges for toll were reduced to nothing, and the trade transported for the mere price of freight, it would be quite practicable, whenever the market at Richmond would possess a superiority of $10 per ton over that of New Orleans, for the line to command the trade of the whole of the valley of the Ohio, below Point Pleasant, and some 300 miles of that of the Mississippi, below the mouth of the former.

*It will be, consequently, practicable for the state of Virginia to enter into successful competition with the city of New Orleans for the whole of the Ohio, and Missouri, and upper Mississippi trade.**

* This result is based on the condition of a superiority of the Richmond market, which is valued at $10 per ton; and for any commodity that is liable to be injured in the southern climate, or that is intended to be re-shipped from New Orleans for the

We shall endeavor shortly to determine, in the present hypothesis, whether or not it will be politic for her to do so.

111. If we now multiply the distance, or length of the valley of the river that will trade with the improvement, by the number of tons per mile which it affords to the trade, we shall have, equation (22)

$$t\, x = t\, \frac{\mathrm{X}\, \pi - h\, \epsilon + \mathrm{M}}{2\, \pi}, \qquad (26)$$

for the equation of the tonnage which will be received at, and transmitted to, the western end of the line.

112. The whole tonnage sent upon the work, multiplied by the charge per ton per mile for toll, will express the revenue per mile which will be derived from this trade on the improvement; and this revenue will consequently be represented by the expression

$$c\, t\, x = c\, t\, \frac{\mathrm{X}\, \pi - h\, \epsilon + \mathrm{M}}{2\, \pi}. \qquad (27)$$

113. The charge which should be levied for the use of the work, in order to render the revenue of the improvement the greatest possible, is a question of primary importance to the stockholder; and it will be obtained by

northern ports, there is but little doubt that the estimate will be found to be quite low enough. For bacon and tobacco, this superiority will be not unfrequently $20.

regarding c as variable, and determining, as in the previous cases, by known rules, the value that should be attributed to it in order to make the above expression a maximum.

The calculation yields for the proper charge on the tonnage derived from the lower Ohio, considered without reference to that from above the outlet of the work,

$$C = \frac{X \pi - h \delta + M}{2 h}, \qquad (28)$$

the toll which will extract the greatest dividend from the trade.

This charge is just one half that for toll which would exclude the trade from the line, equation (24); and we are justified, from the principles which we have laid down, and the deduction in Art. 109, in asserting, that with a difference of $10 per ton in favor of Richmond, *a higher toll than one cent and six mills will not be charged on the principal exports of the west.* We shall hereafter show cause why the toll should be less than this limit.*

114. This value of C being substituted in equation (22), will give for the expression of the portion of the valley which will trade on the improvement,

$$x = \frac{X \pi - h \delta + M}{4 \pi}, \qquad (29)$$

* See § 5.

and consequently, for the tonnage which will be supplied to the line from that distance,

$$T = t. \frac{X \pi - h \delta + M}{4 \pi}. \qquad (30)$$

Or, as we would have anticipated, just half the quantity which would be supplied if the trade were suffered to pass free of toll.

115. I have elsewhere (Art. 98) estimated the whole tonnage of the western waters at about 400,000 tons per annum ; and we shall consequently have, if we neglect the amount received from the upper Mississippi, and consider the above quantity uniformly distributed between New Orleans and Pittsburg, 200 tons per mile for the value of the coefficient t in the preceding equation.

116. With these data, the distance that will be given by equation (29), for the portion of the valley of the Ohio which would use the James River and Kanawha improvement, when the toll is adjusted with a view to the maximum revenue, is 505 miles, and the corresponding trade 101,000 tons. This result is on the supposition, that the advantage possessed by the eastern markets is the same for both the imports and exports of the west. There is, however, a considerable difference between them—in favor of the imports—when the application is made for the northern cities. But it is probable, that the difference will be much less when the Richmond market is the subject of consideration.

117. If we now multiply the above expression of the tonnage, by the most advantageous charge for toll, we shall have the revenue per mile obtained by the improvement, for its conveyance.   This operation yields

$$R = t \frac{(X \, \pi - h \, \delta + M)^2}{8 \, h \, \pi} ; \qquad (31)$$

an equation which shows that the dividend will be much augmented by any diminution of the freight, or length of the line of the improvement, or increase of the value of the market at which it terminates.

118. If, for the sake of an example, we supply the place of the notation by the quantities previously offered, for the James River and Kanawha line, (Art. 106), we shall obtain for the value, in dollars, of this expression of the revenue per mile,

$$R = \$1646,$$

and for the aggregate annual profit derived from this portion of the trade, on the whole line,

$$R \, h = \$765,390.$$

This calculation is offered but for the purpose of an application of the formulæ which have been produced, and others which will be presented hereafter.

The whole course of the investigation must show the impossibility of making a correct estimate of the revenue of a work, without a prior acquaintance with the trade in every article, and the relative merit of the markets in relation to it; since the quantities, and the proper toll, are dependant on these facts.

Throwing out of view, however, the probable influence of rival lines on the north, this result is perhaps as near the truth as the nature of the subject will permit us to come.

119. The known property of quantities susceptible of a maximum, of changing but little in value in consequence of the small changes of the variable at the position of the maximum, deserves to be noticed here in relation to this subject.

A small variation of the charge for toll may be permitted without producing any serious change of the resulting dividend; and it is important to know what effect would be produced in the aggregate revenue, by such a reduction of the charge as would turn the trade of the Mississippi, above the mouth of the Ohio, up that river, and transmit it to Richmond.

For this purpose, we will substitute for x, in equation (22), the distance from Point Pleasant to the mouth of the Ohio—700 miles—and draw from it the corresponding value of $\mathfrak{e}$. We shall obtain from this operation,

$$\mathfrak{e} = 2\tfrac{7}{10} \text{ cents per ton per mile;}$$

and consequently, we shall have for the value of c, which would correspond with this charge,

$$c = 1 \text{ cent per ton per mile.}$$

But the distance is 700 miles, and the tonnage, independently of that above the mouth of the Ohio, must consequently be 140,000 tons.

The revenue due to this tonnage and toll would be $1,400 per mile, and the aggregate revenue on the improvement,

$$\text{R } h = \$651,000.$$

120. Now we have already seen (Art. 113) that the most advantageous toll would be $1\frac{6}{10}$ cents; and that under that charge (Art. 118) the revenue would be $765,390. By such a reduction of the toll as is requisite, under our conditions, to reach the Mississippi trade, it would appear that we lose the amount of $114,390 in revenue, on that of the Ohio; and we increase the tonnage from this river 39,000 tons.

It is probable that this increase of tonnage, though it would afford the company some important incidental advantages, would not be equivalent to the loss of revenue. But I presume that it will hardly be doubted, that the command of the trade of the upper Mississippi and Missouri will afford an ample compensation for the balance. An increase of a very few thousand tons from this source would quite indemnify the company for the loss on the Ohio trade, caused by reducing the toll with a view to obtain that of the Mississippi.

121. Notwithstanding the uncertainty of some part of the data, I feel authorized, from these considerations, to say, that the toll which will be levied on the trade of the

Ohio will be adjusted with a view to obtain that of the
Mississippi above the mouth of the former; and that to
effect this object, *the average toll on the line of the James
and Kanawha improvement, will not exceed one cent per
ton per mile on the leading exports of the west.*

I will add that, under this charge, if the line be constructed in the manner recommended in my report of
the present year, the object will be attained.

122. The preceding investigation is pursued on the
supposition, that the difference in the values of the
markets is the same for all commodities. It need hardly
be said, that in fixing the toll, the actual difference must
be taken, and that it will be found to vary materially
with the nature of the article.

The argument has also been predicated on the supposition, that when the improvement attracts a portion
of the trade, it will attract it all. This, though not
strictly correct, will not be so far from true, as to affect
very materially the results which have been obtained.
If the condition of the work were, like that of Pennsylvania, such as barely to permit it to cope for the trade
around about the western terminus of the line, this
might lead to very important errors. For the point
of division of trade would then be near the end of
the line, and the work would evidently be able to exercise but an imperfect control over its destination. A
part of it would go in one direction, and a part in
the other. But where the trade is supposed to be divided

at a point more than 700 miles from the end of the work, even if the line of division should oscillate over a space of 300 or 400 miles, it would not very materially affect the result. There would still remain 300 or 400 miles of the valley, to trade almost exclusively with the improvement, and the uncertainty would exist only for the balance.

123. We have, in this examination, made no distinction between the prices of ascending and descending freight on the western rivers, because our past experience accords with what we might anticipate, in the conduct of a trade of that nature. There is actually no appreciable difference between the charges in the two directions, although, in either of the two, they are liable to great fluctuations. It might be supposed that, in consequence of the greater resistance in one direction than the other, the charges would necessarily vary likewise ; but, whatever effect this consideration might otherwise have, it is of very little importance, in comparison with the influence of the quantities of freight to be transported.

The charges will usually depend on the demand for boats ; and, consequently, when there is much merchandise to send to the west, the descending freights will be high ; and the ascending will increase when there is much produce to send to the east. And even if the tonnage should happen to be equal in the two directions, the charges would be very nearly equal likewise—for the boat that has the advantage of the fall of the river in one direction, must ascend for its second cargo ; and the cost of the trip will not be very seriously increased by the tonnage taken on board.

The investigation also assumes, that not only the ascending and descending freights are equal, in the same parts of the courses of the rivers, but that the freight above the point of division of trade, is equal to that below.

In the present state of the navigation of the western waters, this assumption is not true at all seasons of the year. But a personal examination of a portion of the Ohio, below the mouth of the Kanawha, has satisfied me of its susceptibility of improvement, to an extent at least sufficient to secure a reduction of the charges down to the limit supposed. And I cannot believe, that a river of which the commerce possesses an importance sufficient to incite to competition all the sea-board states, from South Carolina to New York, and for the attainment of which some millions of dollars are annually expended on the public works of the country, will long continue to need the improvement essential to render these expenditures available. My reasoning, therefore, presupposes an improvement of this navigation adequate to the demands of its commerce.

With these improvements of the Ohio, after the completion of the several competitors for its trade, there will undoubtedly be greater regularity in the business of transportation. This regularity will continue to increase as the system becomes more artificial; and every step which goes to secure the regular delivery of freight, will augment the certainty of particular applications of these principles.

SECTION III.

OF THE TRADE OF THE OHIO, SOUGHT FOR BY TWO RIVAL WORKS.

124. The formulæ deduced in section VI, of the preceding division, are perfectly applicable to this case; but for the sake of distinguishing the notation from that applied to the trade of an improvement, in competition with the river, we will call

> X' the distance from one improvement to the other, by the river;
>
> x' the distance up stream to the dividing point of the trade—the rival being supposed to be situated higher up than the work under consideration;
>
> ε' the cost of transportation on the rival work;
>
> M' the superiority of the market at the terminus of the southern work; and

h, ε, c, δ and π, continuing to represent the same quantities, as in the preceding example.

Then, we shall have by equation (6),

$$x = \frac{X' \, \pi + h' \, \varepsilon' - h \, \varepsilon + M'}{2 \, \pi}, \qquad (32)$$

for the distance to the point of division of the trade.

All the peculiarities of this formula which are essential to our purpose, have been pointed out in the foregoing sections; and the object now need only be, to ascertain what influence the work to which the equation applies will have on the trade of the line below it.

125. The previous applications have been to the James River and Kanawha improvement, and we have seen the extent of the ability of that line to cope with the navigation of the river. We may now learn its ability to compete with the works of Pennsylvania and Maryland.

One of the most important questions in every case, is to ascertain, after the tolls are fixed on the Virginia work, with a view to the maximum revenue from the trade below its entrance into the Ohio, whether it will be able under those charges to secure the trade after it is brought up to the line, or will permit it to pass by and seek that of Pennsylvania.

In general, the Philadelphia market will have a preference, and we have consequently here to attribute a negative value to the quantity represented by M'.

The condition of equality of claims at Point Pleasant, will be expressed by rendering $x' = 0$, in equation (32), from which we will derive

$$M' = X' \pi + h' \mathcal{C}' - h \mathcal{C}. \qquad (33)$$

If, now, we substitute for the charge on the James River and Kanawha improvement, the value of $\mathcal{C}$ under which we are well assured of the control of the trade of the Mississippi, above the mouth of the Ohio, (Art. 119), we shall have for

$$X' \; 260 \text{ miles}, \; h' \; 396 \text{ miles}, \; h \; 465 \text{ miles}, \; \mathcal{C}' = 5 \text{ cents},$$
$$\text{and } \mathcal{C} = 2\tfrac{7}{10} \text{ cents ;}$$

which quantities, substituted in equation (33), will give for the value of M'

$$M' = \$9 \; 20;$$

or, when the charges are regulated on the James River and Kanawha improvement, in the manner that will secure to the line the trade of the Mississippi, the market at Philadelphia must possess a superiority over that of Richmond, equivalent to nine dollars and twenty cents per ton, to enable the present improvement of Pennsylvania to draw any portion of the trade from the valley of the Ohio, below the mouth of the Kanawha.

126. There are few of the heavy products of the west for which such a difference would exist ; and one of the consequences will be, that while the Pennsylvania line continues in its present condition, the trade of the Ohio will flow rapidly to Virginia, and will only be prevented from taking that direction altogether, by the inadequacy of the demand. The Richmond market will sooner become

glutted, and a greater difference of price will follow, until the balance of advantages becomes in favor of its northern rival.

And here we might dilate on the influence that this condition of things will have in building up a market, and drawing the capital necessary to receive and dispose of the trade that may be acquired, and sustain the advantage which a superior position, and it is to be hoped, a more judicious application of its advantages, will have given to the state. But this is a subject that forms no part of the present design.

I believe that any difference that may now exist in the price of the same articles of commerce, between Richmond and the northern ports, will rapidly disappear as the means of obtaining trade—the best encouragement to capital—is more nearly equalized.

If the markets were supposed to possess equal attractions, it could be shown that on the completion of the James River and Kanawha line, the dividing point would fall somewhere near the western base of the Alleghany, on the Conemaugh river, instead of the point last supposed, near the mouth of the Great Kanawha; in other words, that the superiority of the advantages of the Virginia line will be such, that the produce of the Conemaugh above Pittsburg, can be carried down the Ohio and up the Kanawha, and down James River to Richmond, for less than the price at which it is now taken from the Conemaugh to Philadelphia.

The cause of this circumstance is not so much the consequence of the proposed superiority of the construction and design of the Virginia work, as of the unfortunate system of transportation adopted in Pennsylvania, and the plan in use there for crossing the mountain, and passing from the Susquehanna to Philadelphia. *The transportation on that line, combines the slowness of a canal boat with the costliness of rail road carriage.*

127. But, while I am well convinced of the effect which the James River and Kanawha improvement would have on the success of the Pennsylvania works, if the latter were left *in statu quo,* I am equally confident, that such an effect can never be realized for any considerable period. The enterprise of that state, is the surest possible guarantee of the contrary. It is in the power of Pennsylvania to command the trade of the upper Ohio, and at times to share that below, down to the Mississippi; and, I would be the last to doubt, that there is the spirit there that will lead to the application of the means to the purpose.

128. The investigation we have made, should satisfy us, that there is nothing in the present competition of Pennsylvania, to prevent the managers of the James River and Kanawha improvement from levying such toll as the interest of the company may dictate. The influence that limits their charges, and, in fact, controls the subject, is the western navigation ; and the arrange-

ments that are made for procuring the trade, must be regulated with reference to that influence.

129. It will frequently be useful, in the future establishment of the tariff for those lines which terminate on the Ohio, to fix the charges on the trade with a view to obtaining the maximum revenue, from all the tonnage that comes on the line, both from above the entrance of the work, where it is in competition with a rival, and from below, where the issue is between the navigation of the river and the improvement, by an uniform charge.

For this purpose, we are to operate precisely as before, and draw the maximum from the sum of the trade obtained from above and from below the outlet of the work.

By comparing the resulting equation, with the expressions for the toll, on the supposition that a discrimination was made between the charges on the ascending and descending tonnage which would approach the line, we will perceive that the relation which they bear to each other, shows that *the most productive charge common to the trade in both directions, is an arithmetical mean between the charges that should be made on the upper and lower trade, taken separately.*

And by comparing the expression for the tonnage under an uniform charge, applicable to the trade from the north and south, with that which would result from a tariff in which distinct tolls were adopted for the two directions, we will find *that it is precisely the same as if a discrimination had been made in the charges.*

130. The company would however incur a loss of revenue by avoiding such a discrimination ; a fact, indeed, which is strictly applicable to every part of the trade, from one end of the line to the other.

In the case before us, the value of this loss is equal to the difference between the expressions

$$\frac{c + c'}{2} \, (\, x + x' \,) \text{ and } c \, x + c' \, x' \, ;$$

a difference evidently represented by the equivalent value

$$\tfrac{1}{2} \, (\, c - c' \,) \, (\, x - x' \,) \, ;$$

a quantity which increases rapidly with any increase of the difference between the distances from which the article would be brought to the line of the improvement, in the opposite directions.

These facts demonstrate the advantage, in a particular case, which will be found almost universally to have place, of avoiding general and indiscriminate charges in the establishment of a tariff of toll.   It will always be found to promote the interest of a company to proportion the charges on the improvement, to the impediments in the way of the passage of the commodity to a rival line.

131. If a discrimination were made in the tariff of toll, it has been seen that the charge which would yield a maximum revenue, will be, in either direction, half the charge which would entirely exclude the article. But, at the same time, it is evident that the charge on

the trade below the entrance of the work in the Ohio
can never exceed that which would exclude the trade
from above; and the toll on the trade above can never
exceed that which would amount to the exclusion of that
from below;—facts which involve the conclusion that *the
charge on the trade sent from either direction can never
exceed double the most profitable charge on that sent in
the opposite direction.* It might be much less, or nothing,
but never greater than this limit.

132. We perceive here, as in so many other situations,
the unfortunate influence which the introduction of a rival
improvement might have on the prospects of a work;
since it not only divides the trade lying between the two
lines, but, by aiming for that which is beyond its competitor, may exercise a serious control on the toll charged on
every article which it could carry if the other work were
not in existence.

We perceive, also, the necessity of qualifying the conclusion, (Art. 129), that the proper indiscriminate toll
must be an arithmetical mean between the charges which
would be proper for the trade, in case a discrimination were made—since the toll common to the trade
of the two directions, can never exceed the charge which
would exclude that from either direction taken separately—which is the geometrical limitation of the problem.

SECTION IV.

ON THE CORRECTION TO BE APPLIED, WHEN THE
WORK IS FOUND NOT TO BE OPERATING TO THE
BEST ADVANTAGE.

133. The investigation which is presented in Section
II, will lead to some practical results, too important to
the economy of the operation of improvements of this
nature, not to arrest our observation.

The equations which we have given in that division of
the subject, are valuable, as affording the measure of the
influences which the various circumstances under which
the improvement is established, exercise on its success.

They are valuable, also, for the means which they
offer of predicting the event, when we are in possession
of all the data by which it is to be produced.

But we need more than this; we desire some mode of
turning the result of experiment to account, so as to
decide, from the charge actually made, and the tonnage
obtained under that charge, whether there would be any
advantage gained by a modification of the tax levied
upon the trade.

The preceding equations furnish us with the means
of attaining this object.

134. By comparing equations (28) and (29), we will

observe an identity of form, which conducts to some
properties that fulfil this purpose. The numerators of
the second members of these two equations are common ;
and by cancelling them both, we obtain the new expression,

$$C = \frac{2 \pi x}{h} ; \qquad (34)$$

a property necessary to the existence of the condition of
a maximum dividend ; and which shows, that *when the
work is operating under the most advantageous arrangement, the toll on the produce below its outlet into the Ohio,
will be expressed by multiplying twice the freight per ton
per mile on the river, by the distance* below the outlet
from which the article is brought, and dividing by the
length of the improvement.*

By referring to equations (8) and (10), and operating
upon those expressions in the same manner, we will discover, that the value of C which would satisfy the test
for the trade in articles of small value, must be the half
of the quantity represented by equation (34).

135. This property of the preceding equations furnishes us with a very convenient mode of testing the
correctness of the charge which is made, by the actual
effect. For, if we find when the work is fairly in operation, and the trade has taken its direction, and acquired,

* This distance is, of course, the distance to the point where
the direction of the trade changes.

so to speak, its equilibrium, that this equation is not satisfied, we may be pretty well assured that the productiveness of the work will be increased by its modification.

If, for example, we find that when the James River
and Kanawha Company have established a charge of one
cent per ton per mile on flour, that article is brought from
Cincinnati (about 200 miles) to the work, while the
flour below Cincinnati generally goes in the opposite
direction, we shall obtain, by substituting this distance
with the values of π and h, in equation 34,

$$C = \tfrac{5}{8} \text{ of a cent per ton per mile };$$

whereas, if the toll were the most advantageous for the
revenue of the work, this result should have correspond-
ed with the charge actually made, or should have been
one cent per ton per mile.

136. This equation is important, inasmuch as it
relieves us of all the uncertainty which is attendant on
any attempt to make an *à priori* estimate of all the
quantities involved in the other expressions.

The merchant on the Mississippi or Ohio is compe-
tent to decide on the values of all the considerations im-
plicated in those formulæ ; and, in fact, makes his decision in conformity with the knowledge which long
experience, and an intimate acquaintance with the particulars of his business, have provided him. The farmer
who sends his wheat, or the miller who prepares his
flour for the chances of the market, is likewise possessed

of the adequate information ; and if the carriers of their produce are prudent enough to be guided by the decisions based upon the accurate knowledge of these parties, they cannot go far astray.

Indeed, if the people of the west, who send away their produce, or import their merchandise, are them selves in error, it does not affect the question ; for it is their estimate of the values of those quantities, and not the quantities themselves, if the two do not correspond, which governs their decision, and consequently, determines the choice of routes, and the interest of the stockholders of the improvement.

137. The fact that the distance from which any article is brought up the river to the work, or sent down the river into the distant west, is variable ; that it varies with the season, and the state of the markets, and even varies with the views of individuals, does not affect the correctness of the method. It is not an isolated fact which should be taken as the basis of the calculation, but the point at which, during the time when the trade in the article in question is carried on most briskly, seems to divide the directions in which it is forwarded. This point may be a space of a hundred miles ; and if so, it is the centre of that hundred miles which should be employed for the determination of the charge. In all such calculations, it is important first to determine the extremes, and afterward judge from the circumstances, what is the proper average.

138. The preceding equation, (34), furnishes us with the means of testing the correctness of the charge which is levied on any article carried from the Ohio to the Atlantic ; and by pursuing the subject, we will be able to obtain a convenient mode of correcting that charge, if it be found not to satisfy the condition of the maximum of revenue.

If we write equation (28),

$$C = \frac{A}{2h} ;$$

and observe that ε, in equation (22), is equal to $\delta + c$, the latter, which expresses the distance to the place of division under the empirical charge ε, may be put under the form

$$x = \frac{A}{2\pi} - \frac{ch}{2\pi} ;$$

from which we obtain, by cancelling A,

$$C = \frac{\pi x}{h} + \frac{c}{2} ; \qquad (35)$$

in which the values of c and x are known from the experience of the line.

139. This expression affords us a simple practical mode of correcting the charge, when it is found to be incorrect, by the employment of quantities already determined by experiment.

For this purpose, *we ascertain the distance from which the article is brought up the Ohio, when the toll is established at random ; we multiply this distance by the charge for freight on the river, divide by the length of the line of the improvement, and add to the quotient half the previous, or empirical charge for toll.* The result will be the charge which will give the greatest possible dividend.

140. As an example of the application of this formula, we will suppose that the James River and Kanawha Company establish for their average toll on tobacco, three cents per hogshead per mile; and that with this charge, they find that tobacco is drawn to Point Pleasant, from a distance of 300 miles down the Ohio. With these data, equation (34) would give

$$C = \tfrac{9\,0}{9\,3} \text{ of a cent per ton per mile ;}$$

while the charge is actually three cents.

This discrepancy would show the propriety of a modification ; and the same quantities substituted in equation (35), would give

$$C = 1\tfrac{9\,8}{1\,0\,0} \text{ cents per ton per mile,}$$

for the corrected charge, which would be productive of the greatest revenue.

Now, every quantity here is sufficiently known, excepting the distance from which the tobacco is carried up the river ; a portion of the data that might sometimes be difficult to fix with great accuracy.

It might, perhaps, be ascertained that all the tobacco,

or bacon, or any other article found above Louisville, is carried 325 miles up the river, to Point Pleasant, while all
below Evansville, in Indiana, a town 190 miles lower
down the Ohio, is carried in the opposite direction ; and that
the portion which is sent from between those two places,
goes partly in the one direction, and partly in the other.

Now, although this indefiniteness might seem to embarrass the subject, it will rarely, in practice, be productive of difficulty.

If we first assume the nearest point, and make the calculation of the toll that should be charged with reference
to it ; and then the farthest point, and perform a similar
operation, and assume for the correct toll the arithmetical
mean between the two, the result can hardly differ the
value of one mill from the truth.

In the example mentioned above, where the uncertainty is supposed to spread over a space of 190 miles,
the extremes differ less than three mills; and the arithmetical mean differs from either extreme less than one
and a half mills.

141. But to explain the effect of these formulæ, we
may carry out the calculation in the preceding example ;
and by making x in the first instance, 325 miles, or the
distance from Point Pleasant to Louisville, we shall have

$$\mathrm{C} = 2\tfrac{1}{40} \text{ cents,}$$

for the toll which should be charged to make the dividend a maximum, in the event that the charge of 3 cents
was found to bring the article from Louisville.

And by next making x equal to the space of 515 miles, the distance to Evansville, we would obtain

$$C = 2\tfrac{3}{10} \text{ cents,}$$

for the toll which would be productive of the greatest dividend, in the supposition that the charge of 3 cents would bring the article a distance of 515 miles.

142. Now we have supposed, in this example, that there exist an uncertainty in respect to the precise place at which the direction of the trade changes, and that this uncertainty embraces a space of 190 miles, or more than half the distance from the end of the work to the nearest point ; and yet, we perceive, that the difference between the extreme results is but three mills, or about 14 per cent. on the proper charge. In this case, we might take either number without producing any very appreciable change in the dividend which would result from the choice ; and by taking the arithmetical mean between them, the error would be quite imperceptible. That property of quantities susceptible of a maximum, of being slightly affected by a change in the value of the variable when near the position corresponding with the maximum, will be found to prevent any observable error from entering the result.

A very great doubt may exist in regard to the point where the direction of the trade changes ; but any error in the estimate of that distance, will be productive of an error of a lower order in the charge for toll ; and the error in the charge for toll, when the condition of the maximum of revenue is nearly satisfied, will produce an error of a still lower order in the dividend itself.

But, in truth, this distance itself is not so difficult to determine. It is, in general, sufficiently well established ; and any uncertainty which exists will be found to arise from some departure from the common practice, which should not be taken at all into the account.

The fact is then certain, that with a very little care, the toll may be so regulated, that the greatest possible profit may be reaped by the possessors of the improvement, from that portion of this trade which their work accommodates.

143. We may conclude, therefore, that it is generally practicable to correct the charge for toll on a work in actual operation, under these circumstances, if it be found not to be correct ; and that it is always practicable to ascertain, by a simple operation, whether the charge be correct or not.

That the rule for testing the correctness of the tariff is to

Multiply twice the charge for freight on the Ohio, by the greatest distance from which the article is brought up the river to the beginning of the improvement, and divide by the length of the improvement:

If the result be not the identical charge levied, then the work is not operating to the best advantage.

We are also authorised to announce, that in the event of the previous test not being satisfied, the correct charge will be found by

Adding to half the actual charge, the charge for freight on the Ohio, multiplied by the extreme distance from which the article is brought, and divided by the length of the improvement.

If the tonnage in the article be not distributed in the manner supposed in this investigation, a further correction may be applied to the charge obtained by this process, in pursuance of the mode indicated in Part iii, § 5 ; an observation which should receive attention in some of the examples which have been offered in this section.

It may be added, that this method of testing and correcting the tariff from the actual experience of the work, is not limited to the trade of the Ohio or Mississippi, but is applicable to that sought for by competitors in any other part of the line.

The obvious modifications of the formula for this correction, to adapt it to the trade in articles of small value, will be apparent without further illustration.

SECTION V.

OF THE EFFECT OF DEPARTURES FROM THE CHARGE
FOR TOLL CORRESPONDING WITH THE MAXIMUM
REVENUE.

144. I have several times adverted to the peculiarity
of quantities which are susceptible of maxima values, of
being very little affected, when near the maxima, in consequence of any moderate change in the value of the
variable. This fact is important to our pursuit, for various
reasons, but particularly on account of the opportunity it
affords, when the toll is adjusted in the way that will
render the work most productive, of further increasing
the business of the line, without thereby incurring any
sensible diminution of profit.

At every position, and under all possible arrangements,
it may be safely assumed, that an increase of tax for
transportation, will be accompanied by a corresponding
diminution of tonnage ; and it is equally evident, that at
each position there will be, for whatever deficiency occurs
in the tonnage, a more or less adequate compensation to
the stockholders, arising from the greater charge which
will be levied upon the trade actually obtained ; and that,
if the toll be diminished, for whatever falling off there

may be in the profit per ton, there will be a certain compensation in the increased number of tons.

145. This reasoning is perfectly sound ; but yet there is only one position for each article, at which such an increase or diminution may be made without a sensible, and frequently a very serious sacrifice of the interests of the stockholders. This point is that at which the toll will yield the greatest possible dividend.

146. To learn the effect of this departure, we must observe the form of the general expression of the tonnage from the Ohio, which is given in equation (26), where, it will be recollected, the value of ς is $\delta + c$.

If in this equation we make c take the increment c', which we will here suppose to be negative, we shall obtain the effect of the change on the tonnage, by deducting the preceding equation from its new value—an operation which will show the increase of trade to be expressed by

$$t\,\frac{c'h}{2\pi}; \qquad\qquad (36)$$

or, *a reduction of the charge for toll on the trade derived from any branch, will increase the tonnage of the line an amount equal to the whole quantity furnished by a portion of the tributary of which the length is that of the improvement, multiplied by the ratio of the diminution of the charge, to twice the charge for freight on the tributary.*

147. To give an example of this statement,—if this change be one mill per ton per mile, the ratio of that reduction to twice the freight on the Ohio, will be the fraction $\frac{1}{15}$; and this fraction multiplied by the length of the improvement, say 465 miles—the length of the James River and Kanawha line—will give 31 miles of the valley of the Ohio, for the increase consequent on this modification of the toll. This distance, at 200 tons per mile, will furnish an additional amount of trade of 6200 tons.

148. We will next observe that the maximum revenue is expressed by the equation deduced in Art. 117; and the toll under which it is obtained, by equation (28), of Art. 113.

If we now suppose this toll to receive the negative increment c', we shall have for the new expression of the revenue, equation (27),

$$ R' = t \; \frac{X \, \pi - h \, \varepsilon + M}{2 \, \pi} \; (C - c') $$

where the general value of c in the equation is represented by the particular value $C - c'$.

If we make this substitution, and deduct the latter value of the revenue from that which it possesses at its maximum, we shall find for the difference

$$ t. \; \frac{h \, c'^{\,2}}{2 \, \pi} ; \qquad (37) $$

or, *when the toll is reduced below the charge which would
produce the greatest dividend, the diminution of revenue
per mile will be represented by the increased tonnage due to
the reduction of the toll, multiplied by the amount of its
reduction.*

149. Applying this result to the preceding example,
Art. 147, where a diminution of toll equal to one mill produced an increase of trade of 6200 tons, we shall have
for the deficiency of revenue

$6 20 per mile.

Thus, we perceive, that when the proper charge is
made on the James River and Kanawha line, a reduction
of one mill per ton per mile in the toll will increase the
trade of the work about six thousand tons, and produce a reduction of the revenue of but six dollars per
mile; or, *at this position, a departure from the most advantageous toll of about 6 per cent., and from the whole
tax on the trade of about 3 per cent., will affect the
aggregate revenue of that line but about one third of
one per cent.*   (See Section II.)

These results, it must be remembered, are obtained
without considering the incidental advantages which
accrue from an increase of trade,—a subject which shall
presently occupy our attention—nor the slight increase of
the trade itself caused by the wider space from which it
will be carried laterally to the Ohio.

150. By recurring again to the form of equation (37),

we will remark that *the loss of revenue caused by a departure from the most profitable toll, increases as the
square of the amount of the departure;* and that, although a change of one mill would, in our example, produce a deficiency of revenue of but six dollars and twenty
cents per mile, a change of one cent would produce a
difference of one hundred times that amount, or six hundred and twenty dollars per mile.   And this last difference,
on the whole line of the James River and Kanawha improvement, supposing it to be in successful operation,
would amount to no less than two hundred and eighty-
eight thousand three hundred dollars.

We need no better evidence of the necessity of a judicious tariff of toll, and a proper understanding of the
laws of trade, to enable a company to take advantage of
their position in the field of competition ; and we shall see,
before long, that such information is as essential to every
other step of the progress of the engineer, in the dis-
charge of his duties.

151. To render more palpable the fact above adverted
to, that the loss of revenue resulting from any departure
from the proper tariff, is much less near the position
which accords with the maximum, than at points removed from that position, we will make further application of the preceding equation.

At the most advantageous position a reduction of one
mill might have no serious effect ; but after first aber-

rating nine mills, an error of an additional mill would have a very conspicuous influence.

This fact may be conveniently explained by making the reduction of charge designated by c' take any other value c''; and we shall then have for the difference between the amounts of falling off of revenue in the two cases, the expression,

$$\frac{t\,h}{2\,\pi}\,(c'^2 - c''^2). \qquad (38)$$

To apply this formula, we will suppose the charge in the first place to differ from that which would yield the greatest revenue, the amount represented by c'', which we will suppose to be nine mills; and in the second place, that designated by c', or one cent.

We shall then have for the difference of revenue per mile, on the Ohio trade, due to a change of one mill in the charge for toll, in this situation,

$$\$117\tfrac{80}{100};$$

or, when the charge is already nine mills less than it ought to be to yield the greatest revenue, an error of an additional mill, will produce an additional deficiency of nearly one hundred and eighteen dollars per mile; or nineteen times the effect produced by the same alteration near the maximum.

152. The result of the investigation must satisfy us, it is thought, that the charges should generally be less than

those which would conform precisely with the maximum.

There are many reasons why this should be so, but the fact that the revenue will be but little diminished by such an arrangement, and a very material increase of tonnage will result from the measure, are important arguments in its favor.

At the same time, I am under the impression that there is a sufficiently distinct limit, which marks the extent proper for such departures from the result of the calculation. This limit is so well defined, that we can scarcely doubt what ought to be the policy of those who manage the affairs of the improvement, with whatever view it may be constructed.

A certain sacrifice of revenue may, under many circumstances, be admitted for the purpose of increasing the trade; but the extent of the sacrifice must always be confined to a very contracted range.

On the James River and Kanawha improvement, when in competition only with the western navigation, in the example just offered, a departure of four mills on each ton, or a reduction equal to one fourth the toll after the maximum is obtained, would involve an apparent loss of about $46,128 per annum on the trade of the lower Ohio; but after that sacrifice, which would be a judicious one, is incurred, an additional reduction of only two mills would bring about an additional reduction of revenue, of about $57,660, and increase the trade only half as much as the former reduction. Beyond this point, any further reduction would be injurious to the work in a much higher amount; and would, withal, be productive of an advantage, in the increase of business, only proportional to the reduction. In other words, *the tonnage is augmented a quantity proportional to the departure from the limit assigned by the formula, and the revenue is diminished proportionally to the square of the same departure.*

I am of opinion that, in general, 25 per cent. is as much as it will be found judicious to adopt for the departure from the scale authorized by the investigation for the toll which will yield the greatest revenue, on most articles constituting the heavy trade of the Ohio.

The same remark will probably be true of the merchandise sent to the west; for the difference between the charges on that branch of the trade, and on the western exports, is probably not destined to long continuance. The tolls on the transportation of this portion will be brought down nearer to the level of those on the grosser products, by the additional competition that will be offered for it by the rail road lines, which will be unable to participate in other divisions of the trade.

153. There are many reasons in favor of the policy of reducing the toll below the limit most advantageous to the revenue of the work, given by the principles adopted in this volume. But it is essential first to know the charge which these principles would authorize, before we can

determine how much it would be wise to reduce it. The reduction should be proportional to the amount from which it is made.

Let us suppose for a moment, that we had determined, from a careful calculation, the charge which our equations would indicate to be the most advantageous for the dividend ; and that the tariff for the coal and ore, iron, plaster and wheat, had been regulated with a view to the greatest possible profit under the distribution assumed for the tonnage. On further investigation, we would discover causes for a modification, and, very generally, for a reduction of the charges established.

We would observe, for instance, that the toll on plaster might give the greatest revenue for the year in question, and for that article taken separately : but that if the charge on each ton were reduced, it would be carried a greater distance on the line, and a greater distance into the interior, to the right and left ; that some farmers who had not been able to obtain it before, could now enrich their lands by its use, and others who had previously used but a small amount, could now increase their purchases ; and that, although a slight loss would perhaps be experienced in the immediate toll, the company would be indirectly remunerated by the augmented crop of wheat springing from its application.

The increased supply of wheat would not only pay them again in toll, but would be productive of an increased demand for water for its manufacture. The water would remunerate the company again in rents, and perhaps in the further manufacture of articles on which toll could be levied.

The additional wheat would produce additional straw, and chaff and bran. The straw would go to the further enrichment of the soil, and the reproduction of increased crops ; the bran to the production of stock, and the stock again to the improvement of the soil. The tanneries are brought into operation by the same cause, and the bark that supplies them increases the toll. Barrels are needed for the flour, tolls are received from the barrels, and water power is purchased for the production of the staves.*

The operation of the same influence—the reduction of toll on manure—might be traced in other directions, and to other varieties of produce, and would result in showing the infinite modes in which the income of the company might be augmented by a diminution of its immediate revenue on one item.

154. If we trace the passage of the ore from the mine to its numerous applications to the mechanic arts, we will find it not less interesting, and the profits of the improvement not less involved in its various transformations. A reduction of the toll on this article will increase its consumption at the furnace located on the borders of the

---

* There are usually carried from 200,000 to 300,000 *staves*, and more than 100,000 *hoop poles*, annually to Richmond by the James River and Kanawha Canal.

canal; the proprietor of the furnace pays for the water employed for the blast; the product of the furnace augments the revenue in its transportation to the rolling-mill or trip hammer, and a new demand for water is created at the forge.

The activity of the operations at the collieries is augmented to furni h the fuel necessary for the conversion of the ore into metal, or the forests are levelled for the purpose, and new tracts of land thence brought under tillage. The increased operations at the various establishments through which the mineral passes, creates new demand for the machinery needed for their duties, and the talents of the artisan, and the labor of the mechanic, are brought into requisition.

The proprietors of the numerous establishments called into existence by this policy, soon find that their interests will be promoted by an extension of their business; and the power thus created, and the materials that are furnished, for the supply of a limited local demand, become shortly applied to the competition for foreign markets.

The population is increased, and consequently the products of the labor, and the wants of society, are at the same time augmented.

Such effects are in the first place brought about by the improvement itself, in reducing the cost of transportation, and offering facilities for the profitable application of capital and labor; and analogous results spring from each successive reduction of the charges on the line.

And so far, they are to be regarded as arguments in favor of keeping always within the limit assigned by the geometrical principles which have controlled our investigations.

155. Independently of these considerations, there are others which militate in favor of the same policy, growing out of the constitution of the corporations by which the great lines of improvement of the country are generally constructed.

Such works are rarely, if ever, undertaken exclusively as objects of immediate speculation. Capital is too valuable here to be invested in enterprises which can at best be expected to return but a moderate interest, and that at a day so distant, that the capitalist looks upon his subscription rather as the property of his heirs than himself. And in consequence, investments are seldom made in such objects with a view to the immediate profitableness of the venture as an interest paying fund.

The stock is held by the individuals whose business is to be enhanced, or whose vacant grounds are to be brought into market, by the growth of the city at the outlet of the improvement, or at the points which are to receive peculiar benefit from the trade of the region through which it is conducted; by the banks that are connected in business with the corporation, and whose operations are to be increased by the general expansion of trade consequent on its ultimate success; by the sea-ports at which they terminate, whose existence as cities depends on the successful accomplishment of the design, and whose interest in the project, independently of their interest as stockholders, is directly as the trade which they owe to its completion ; and finally, by the commonwealth itself, whose interest as a partial proprietor is of the same character, to the extent to which it reaches, as if it were the sole possessor of the work.

The interest of the proprietors of the improvement, apart from that which they possess in the value of the stock, is of various descriptions, and of a character to which it is difficult to assign a value; but it is, to express the idea in mathematical language, a function of the charges upon the line; and consequently, must be regarded in arranging the tariff of toll. For, if after the most advantageous charge in reference to the location and character of the trade is determined, it be found that a certain reduction would produce a certain increase of trade, and that any stockholder would gain more by the increase of the profits of his business due to the change, than he would lose by the diminution of his dividend ; then, so far at least as that individual is concerned, it would be proper to make the reduction. And considering the constitution of such corporations, it appears to be probable that there are few connected with them whose interests would not be individually affected in this way.

156. Although these influences are adverted to for the

purpose of showing the propriety of adopting the practice recommended, of keeping always below the limits prescribed by the formulæ, it is not to be overlooked that the surest course will be to avoid a wide departure from those limits. It is to be remembered, that after we have once determined the toll corresponding with the maximum, any further reduction will increase the trade directly as the value of the departure from the maximum, and reduce the revenue in the duplicate ratio of the departure. This is a principle that can be well established, and an expression of loss that can be securely estimated; while those circumstances that would seem to authorize a reduction are of doubtful value, and perhaps not always beneficial to all the members of the corporation. I will repeat the opinion, that it will rarely be found advisable to vary more than 25 per cent. from the charge that would be obtained from the strict application of these principles.

157. It must be apparent from all that has preceded, how uncertain will be any attempt to establish a tariff of charges, founded, as is sometimes the practice, on the value of the articles transported.

The true basis of the tariff which is made with a view to the promotion of the interest of the stockholders, is the necessities of the trade; and the determination of the highest tax that ought to be levied upon it, under this view of the subject, can, I think, only be properly made by the principles which I have endeavored to explain.

Doubtless, if the tolls be established after these principles, they will generally be found to be somewhat affected by the values of the commodities—since that freight which is not an object of the competition of rival lines will necessarily, by the formulæ, be charged less than that which is,—the two being carried the same distance on the line,—and of that which is not the subject of such competition, the commodities that are the most valuable in themselves will generally bear the highest charges, in the sense in which the expression is used in the examination.

158. The application of these views must satisfy the mind, that when the true interest of the improvement is consulted, there is little probability that the trade will be crippled by excessive taxation. The very nature of the research, and the foundation of the investigation, is opposed to such a result. We start with the admission of the impropriety of over charges, and fix a limit below which it will always be proper to keep them.

The danger to be apprehended on this score, is rather applicable to the practice of fixing empirical rates ; since the opinion is too likely to prevail, in a popular view of the subject, that an increase of toll will be followed by an increase of revenue, without a premising of those qualifications which a correct investigation of the question will show to be proper.

The distant trade is particularly secure against this source of apprehension : that of the Ohio is always safe ; and it may be asserted as a general fact, that *on*

*the James River and Kanawha improvement, the tolls
will always be less than 5½ mills per ton per mile on all
articles brought from the Ohio, which would command the
same price at New Orleans as at Richmond.* And it will
hereafter be demonstrated by the application of the preceding formulæ, that *for every dollar that the value of the
Richmond market exceeds that of New Orleans on any
commodity, the toll will be increased a fraction over one
mill per ton per mile.*

If my estimate of the charge for freight on the Pennsylvania improvement be correct, that line can obtain no
trade whatever, if there be any toll levied, unless the
market at Philadelphia have a preference for the article
to be bought or sold, of more than three dollars per
ton ; and, for every dollar per ton over three dollars, by
which the Philadelphia market exceeds that of New
Orleans, the toll on that line may be increased 1¼ mills
per ton per mile.*

---

* In this passage, as in every other in which the Pennsylvania improvement is adverted to, the conclusions are obtained
in reference to the present work, and the system of transportation adopted on it. The author has elsewhere stated the amend-
ments of which he thinks the line itself susceptible, and he
does not hesitate to aver that the revenue of all the improvements of that state may be more than doubled by mere modifications of the tariff of toll, and a reformation in the system of
transportation, without incurring an additional expense of one
dollar for construction.

These are general average results of quantities susceptible of considerable variation ; but if they are not strictly accurate, they are near enough to the truth to show the security of the distant trade.

NOTE.—In the preceding applications of the formulæ to the James River and Kanawha line, no distinction is made between that portion of the charge for freight which is constant, and that which varies with the trade. This is neglected because, in the first place, the expenses which are independent of the amount of business on the line would be very small, in comparison with the aggregate charge for freight ; and it may be shown by the formulæ, that no appreciable difference can be remarked in the resulting dividend, whether this distinction be made or neglected. And in the second place, because the consequence of assuming the larger number will be to produce for the toll corresponding with the maximum revenue, a sum rather below its true geometrical value—in which it has been proved, there will be some advantage.

PART III.

PRACTICAL ILLUSTRATIONS.

SECTION I.

OF THE INFLUENCE OF CHANGES IN THE PRICE OF
FREIGHT ON THE OHIO AND MISSISSIPPI.

159. It may appear that the simplicity of the results
which have been obtained, might render superfluous any
further discussion of the equations that expose the laws
which are the objects of this investigation. There are,
however, some views which have not yet been presented,
following as consequences of our premises, of such great
importance to the interest of the subject, that I will venture still to offer them.

The fact, that changes will take place in the tonnage
of the line, in the toll that ought to be exacted, and in the
revenue that is received, in consequence of any circumstance influencing the value of the charges on the trade,
is easily perceived. But the measure of those changes ;
the amount that the toll, tonnage and revenue will be in-

creased or diminished, in consideration of any modification of the conditions under which the transportation is
effected, is not so obvious.

It is the object of the examination immediately before
us, to determine the value of these influences by the
most accurate method for our adoption ; and to illustrate
their importance by conspicuous examples.

In stating the probable result on the James River and
Kanawha improvement—the toll that would be charged,
and the tonnage and revenue that would be obtained—
the price of freight on the Ohio and Mississippi was assumed at three quarters of a cent per ton per mile.
The sum is perhaps as near the present average charge,
in good water, as any we are able to obtain.   But, as this
element is liable to some variation, it is desirable to ascertain what influence its changes may have on the operations of the improvement the trade of which is subject
to the charge.

160. If we inspect the form of the expression of the
toll on the lower Ohio trade, when the revenue is a maximum, which is given in equation (28), we will observe,
that the charge will evidently increase with every augmentation of the price of freight on the river.

And if we suppose this freight to receive an increase,
which we will represent by the increment π', the corresponding change of the value of C will be expressed by

$$C' - C = \frac{X}{2h}\pi' ; \qquad (39)$$

or, *the toll per ton per mile on the improvement will be augmented by any increase of freight on the river, an amount obtained by multiplying the distance from the outlet of the work to New Orleans by the increase of the price of freight, and dividing by twice the length of the improvement.*

161. For the James and Kanawha improvement the ratio of the distance to New Orleans to twice the length of the improvement, would be $\frac{29}{16}$, and *the increase of toll on that work will therefore be twenty-nine sixteenths the increase of freight on the river.*

So that if the charges on the Ohio should generally receive an increase or reduction of five mills, all the tolls on this work ought to take a simultaneous increase or reduction of nine mills.

It is hardly necessary to observe that this remark is not intended to apply to temporary and partial fluctuations in the freights; but to such changes as would be produced by a general falling off or improvement of the navigation, whether by increasing or removing the impediments in the river, or by an increase or diminution of competition caused by a general accession or withdrawal of capital from the steamboat companies.

It must be obvious, also, that *general* fluctuations of the price of freights on the western waters must be very limited in extent. From one to two mills per ton per mile, I would suppose, after the improvement of the river, will be found to be the extreme of such variations.

162. The expression of the distance along the river, the trade of which would be commanded by the improvement when operating most profitably, (equation 29), may be written,

$$x = \frac{X}{4} + \frac{M - h\,\delta}{4\,\pi};$$

from which it is evident that any diminution of the charge for freight on the steamboats, will have the effect of increasing the tonnage so long as we have

$$M > h\,\delta.$$

We have hitherto supposed 1000 cents to be the mean value of M for the heavy products of the west, and 790 that of $h\,\delta$, on the James River and Kanawha line.

If this be correct, a decrease of the cost of freight on those rivers would rather increase the tonnage than otherwise; and we have already seen that such a reduction of the charge would reduce the toll on the work. Since then, any depression of the charge for freight must itself be very small, and when it does occur, is likely to affect the toll and the tonnage with contrary signs, we are authorized to assert, that the conclusions at which we have arrived will be but little influenced by any reduction of freights on the western waters.

There is not likely ever to be any permanent general augmentation of freights; since the only changes of the actual condition of things are to be looked for as the results of the progressive amelioration of the state of the navigation, the increase of competition, or improvements in the application of steam.

We must not, however, forget in the present application of the mode of calculation here adopted, that excepting in good stages of the water, there is a noted difference between the cost of freight on the upper and lower portions of the river. When the stream is swollen, there is no such difference perceptible ; and when the upper portions of the Ohio are adequately improved, there will probably be none such at any period of the year.

It is presumed hardly necessary to add that the foregoing results are only applicable to the trade which will admit of competition ; and that the tonnage which will bear but a limited charge, is not to be considered to participate in the conclusions which we have announced.

SECTION II.

OF THE EFFECT OF CHANGES IN THE PRICE OF FREIGHT ON THE IMPROVEMENT.

163. Though nearly all that need be added on this branch of the subject might be anticipated from what has preceded, I am induced by its great and vital importance in the whole policy of internal improvement, to regard it more closely.

Of all the questions that arise in the establishment of a plan of improvement, this is undoubtedly that which, on the long lines of this country, exercises the most controlling influence.

A variation of the length of the work affects, of course, the tonnage and the toll proportionally to the amount of the variation; but the difference in length between two lines of the same system, running between the same points, can rarely be very great, and the influence of that consideration is consequently, for the most part, quite limited.

The permanent changes of the relative values of markets are likewise usually confined to oscillations of not very considerable extent; and even where more important changes do occur, the interest injured may frequently find some mode of indemnification.

But the influence of changes in the rates of freight extends over the whole line, and applies to every foot that every ton is conveyed. And these rates depend mainly on the system that is selected, and are, of course, irremediable when once established.

Before a work is commenced, the propriety of its being undertaken turns on the value of this charge; after its construction is decided on, the selection of a system of improvement depends on it; and after the selection is made, the details of the location are influenced by the same consideration. If it be a rail road, the acclivity of the grades to be admitted depends in part

on this value, and if it be a canal, the very capacity
of the work rests upon it.

164. Taking again the general expression of the toll
on an improvement in competition with a rival line with
which it is connected, which, under our hypothesis, will
be productive of the greatest profit, we shall have by
equation (28), the value of the charge for the trade of
the lower part of the Ohio ; and if we suppose that from
any circumstance the value of δ, or the charge for
freight, receive a negative increment which is represented
by — δ', we shall have for the corresponding toll,

$$C' = \frac{X\,\pi - h\,(\delta - \delta') + M}{2\,h}.$$

It is evident that since δ' is negative, C' is here greater
than C, or that the most advantageous charge per ton
per mile which can be levied for the interest of the
owners of the improvement, will be increased by the diminution of the charge for freight.

By taking the difference between the above expression
and that of equation (28), we shall obtain for the augmentation of toll per ton per mile caused by the diminution δ'
of the actual cost of carriage,

$$C' - C = \frac{\delta'}{2}\,; \qquad\qquad (40)$$

or, *the toll on the whole of the trade obtained in the
competition with a rival ought to be increased just half
as much as the charge for freight is diminished.*

165. If we next take the expression of the whole charge to which the article is subjected when the revenue is the greatest, which we have given in equation (13), and suppose, as before, δ to become $\delta - \delta'$, and substitute this new value in the equation, we shall obtain, by taking the difference,

$$\epsilon - \epsilon' = \frac{\delta'}{2}, \qquad (41)$$

for the diminution of the whole charge due to δ', the decrease of the charge for freight.

We find, therefore, that *any diminution in the charge for freight will increase the profit on the improvement just half as much as the freight is diminished, and diminish the whole tax to which the commodity is subjected just as much as the toll is increased.*

166. If we apply the same method to the expression of the toll and tax on the trade that will bear but limited charges, we shall find the same results; so that, for whatever portion of the business of an improvement the law of the distribution of tonnage is that on which these remarks are based, the conclusions announced above will hold true.

167. As an evidence of the importance of reducing the price of freight, and a suitable application of these results, we may refer to some of the charges on the Pennsylvania improvement for the exports of the west.

The whole charge for the conveyance of bacon, and

other heavy products, from Pittsburg to Philadelphia, is
87½ cents per 100 lbs. ; or about 5 cents per ton per mile ;
and the canal and rail road toll received by the state on the
same commodities is about 1¼ cents per ton per mile.   So
that, out of every five cents that the article is taxed, the
state receives but one and a quarter cents, and out of this
modicum she must keep her works in repair, and maintain
her agents and superintendants on the line.

It is not possible to determine the precise portion of this
toll that actually goes into the treasury, and the part that
goes to the repairs and other expenses for the maintenance of the works.   But I think it would be difficult to
establish the fact, that the commonwealth receives a clear
profit—all expenses being paid—of a half cent per ton
per mile on all articles conveyed.   Assuming, however,
that the profit is one half cent, we shall have $\varsigma = 5$ cents
per ton per mile, and (supposing the toll now to be
properly adjusted) $C = \frac{1}{2}$ cent.

The charge for freight on this improvement is, then,
according to the definition we have adopted, 4½ cents per
ton per mile.

Let us now suppose that an improvement could be
made which would reduce the freight down to what
we have assumed for a canal, or 1¼ cents per ton per
mile.   We should then have $\delta' = 3\frac{1}{4}$ cents, and the
changes consequent on such an improvement,

$$\varsigma - \varsigma' = \frac{3\frac{1}{4}}{2} \text{ and } C' - C = \frac{3\frac{1}{4}}{2};$$

from which we immediately obtain for the toll, or clear profit on the new improvement,

$$C' = 2\tfrac{1}{8} \text{ cents,}$$

and for the whole tax on the commodity conveyed,

$$\mathfrak{E}' = 3\tfrac{3}{8} \text{ cents ;}$$

and, of course, for the freight,

$$\delta = 1\tfrac{1}{4} \text{ cents.}$$

So that, if there were a good canal from Philadelphia to Pittsburg, 396 miles long, the produce, instead of being taxed, as now, 5 cents per ton per mile, would be charged but $3\tfrac{3}{8}$ cents ; instead of a toll, or clear profit of $\tfrac{1}{2}$ cent, would pay the state $2\tfrac{1}{8}$ cents, or more than four times as much as it now pays, and instead of a consumption of charges in the labor and profits of carriage, of $4\tfrac{1}{2}$ cents, there would be appropriated but $1\tfrac{1}{4}$ cents to that object.

168. These remarks apply to the whole of the Ohio trade, and to the trade of any line communicating with another port, and, as we perceive, to all the tonnage which will bear but a limited charge for transportation, without any regard to the mode in which it reaches the improvement.

The only portions of the articles carried on the line which escape the application of the principles we have adopted, are that part adverted to in section (10), Part I, which is situated so near the origin of the improvement that the charges indicated by the condition of a maximum evenue, would exceed the power of the company to levy ; and that portion of the trade, if there be any such portion, of which the quantity is independent of the cost of conveyance.

169. The expression for the tonnage obtained from the lower part of the Ohio, when the work is supposed to be operating to the best advantage, is given in equation (30).

Making the same substitution of $\delta - \delta'$ for δ, we shall have for the new value of the tonnage,

$$t\, x' = t\, \frac{X\, \pi - h\,(\delta - \delta') + M}{4\, \pi}.$$

It is evident here also that x' is greater than x, or that the business of the line is augmented by the reduction of the charge for freight.

If we deduct the preceding value of the tonnage from that which it becomes by the variation in the cost of carriage, we shall have

$$t\,(x' - x) = t\, \frac{h\,\delta'}{4\,\pi}, \qquad (42)$$

for the increase of the trade due to the reduction δ' of the charge for freight.

And if we take the value of the tonnage represented by equation (10), applicable to the condition of the trade which is not an object of competition, and perform the same operation, we shall obtain for the result,

$$t\ (x' - x) = t\ \frac{h\ \delta'}{2\ \beta}\ ;\qquad (43)$$

or, the acquisition of tonnage due to such a change, will in this case be twice as great as in the preceding, if the cost of transportation on the lateral branches be the same in both instances.

170. Equation (42) teaches us that *any reduction of the price of carriage on the work will be productive of an augmentation of trade represented by all the tonnage that would be supplied to the improvement, from a distance along the valley of the Ohio, equal to one fourth the length of the line of the improvement, mul tiplied by the ratio of the fall in the price of freight on the work, to the charge for freight on the river.*

For example, if the reduction of the freight on the line were two and a half mills, this ratio would be the fraction $\frac{1}{3}$; and one fourth the length of the line of the James River and Kanawha improvement is $116\frac{1}{4}$ miles ; so that, in this case, a fall of $2\frac{1}{2}$ mills in the price of freight would give the company the trade of an additional distance of $38\frac{2}{3}$ miles of the valley of the Ohio ; or, at 200 tons per mile, would increase the tonnage 7740 tons.

We have seen, by the preceding articles, that this reduction of freight would, at the same time, increase the profits $1\frac{1}{4}$ mills per ton per mile, and diminish the whole tax on the trade an equal amount.

171. For an additional example, let us suppose, as before, that improvements might be made on the principal line of Pennsylvania, which would reduce the freights down to the cost of transportation on a continuous canal from Philadelphia to Pittsburg; a change which we have already stated at about $3\frac{1}{4}$ cents per ton per mile.

This value of δ' being substituted in equation (42), will give (neglecting the coefficient of tonnage),

$$x' - x = 503\frac{2}{3} \text{ miles };$$

or, the trade of $503\frac{2}{3}$ miles of the valley of the Ohio. This distance would furnish at least 100,733 tons, a quantity that would at once be thrown upon the line; and this additional quantity, together with the trade which that improvement obtains by its present facilities, would yield the commonwealth a clear profit of $2\frac{1}{8}$ cents per ton per mile, instead of about $\frac{1}{2}$ cent, as at present, and reduce the whole tax now levied on the commerce of the west, not less than $1\frac{5}{8}$ cents per ton per mile.

I have before explained why the reduction of the charges should be greater than is called for by the condition of rendering the revenue the greatest possible; and if the toll were regulated on a continuous canal in Pennsylvania, with a view to the most profitable result, it is probable that this tonnage would be considerably increased. But we need not here repeat the considerations connected with this subject.

172. The expression of the maximum revenue per

mile on the trade below the outlet of the improvement on the Ohio, has been given in Art. 117, and if we again suppose, as before, the freight δ to take the new diminished value $\delta - \delta'$, and draw from this equation the expression of the revenue after the reduction, and subtract the preceding value from it, we shall have for the difference,

$$R' - R = \delta' \left(\frac{X\pi - h\delta + M}{4\pi} t + \frac{h\delta'}{8\pi} t \right); \quad (44)$$

which is the expression of the increase of revenue per mile due to the reduction δ' of freight.

If we compare the first member of this formula with equation (30), we will find that it is no other than the expression of the tonnage before the reduction of the charge ; and the second member, compared with equation (42), will show us that it stands for half the increase of tonnage due to the reduction.

If we then call T the tonnage before the change, we may write the above expression

$$R' - R = T\delta' + t\frac{h\delta'}{8\pi}\delta' ; \quad (45)$$

from which we learn, that *the increase of revenue per mile which may be anticipated from a general reduction of the charge for freight on the improvement, will be equal to the arithmetical mean between the values of the tonnage before and after the reduction, multiplied by the whole amount that the freight per mile is reduced.*

173. When the change in the price of freight is very small, it will be permitted to neglect the second member of equation (45), and say simply that *the revenue will be increased by any small reduction of the cost of carriage, an amount equal to the whole tonnage of the line multiplied by the value of the reduction;* a fact that is expressed by

$$R' - R = T \, h \, \delta', \qquad (46)$$

where the application is made to the whole length of the line.*

This, and some similar conclusions which will be obtained in the next pages, may be arrived at by a more direct process, without the aid of analytical argument. But it is to be observed, that the fact here announced, is asserted to exist simultaneously with a *reduction* of the whole tax on the article, equal to the sum that the toll or profit is *increased*, and with an augmentation of trade due to this reduction of the whole tax, expressed by equation (42). It is perfectly apparent, that if we reduce

---

* Although this result is obtained in the supposition that the charge for toll receive a modification for every variation of the charge for freight, such modification is not essential to the attainment of the limit expressed by equation (46). This fact is apparent on a little reflection, and is easily susceptible of demonstration by the formulæ.

the charge for freight, we may add the amount it is reduced to the toll, and in that way increase the revenue
the quantity stated above.   But this operation obliges us
to maintain the whole charges on the trade at their former value.   The investigation teaches that *the reduction of freight will augment the revenue an amount
equal to the whole reduction—increase the toll per ton
per mile an amount equal to half the reduction per ton
per mile—diminish the aggregate charges as much
as the toll is increased, and augment the business
an amount due to the diminished tax upon the trade.*
And it is also to be observed that the above is only the
lowest limit of the measure of the advantage gained by
such reduction ; and that when this reduction is considerable, we are to have recourse to the higher expression
of equation (45).

174. For an example, let us suppose that while the
James River and Kanawha improvement is receiving
100,000 tons from the Ohio, a reduction of $2\frac{1}{2}$ mills per
ton per mile is in some way produced in the ex-
pense of freight.   We have already seen, (Art. 170), that
the change here indicated would produce a corresponding
accession of trade, of 7740 tons ; so that we should have,
in this case,

$$(100,000 + 3870) \; 2\tfrac{1}{2} \text{ mills} = \$259 \; 67\tfrac{1}{2}$$

per mile ; or a decrease of only one fourth of a cent per
ton per mile in the cost of carriage, would produce an

increase of profit to the company, of more than one hundred and twenty thousand dollars per annum on the Ohio trade alone.

And for an additional example, we will take the case already cited, of the Pennsylvania improvement,—where a reduction of $3\frac{1}{4}$ cents per ton per mile might be effected by the substitution of a continuous canal in place of the present broken line.

This reduction, it has been shown in Art. 171, would increase the tonnage from the Ohio 100,733 tons; and our formula will consequently give for the increase of revenue, if we call the present trade 60,000 tons,

$$R' - R = (60,000 + 50,366) \; 3\tfrac{1}{4} = \$3,587 \text{ per mile };$$

which, for the whole length of the line, would amount to the sum of $1,667,955, on the Ohio trade alone.

I do not doubt that the execution of a canal from Philadelphia to Pittsburg, would have a much greater influence than this on the revenue of that commonwealth; the application is only made to that work for the purpose of an additional practical illustration of the consequences of a reduction of the charges.

175. If it were necessary to go further into this matter, we might sum up the increase of tonnage and revenue affected by a diminution of freight, on all the tributaries to the line; but it is believed that enough has been said to demonstrate the importance of the subject.

The interest of the proprietors of the improvement,

whether they be the commonwealth or a company, must suffer from any diminution of the tonnage, beyond the mere value of the decrease of revenue which we perceive would result from it.

The interest of the cities to which the trade is carried depends on its amount; and the interest of the citizens engaged in its transportation, is affected just in the proportion that the diminution bears to the original quantity.

As the trade is reduced, there is a proportionally less incitement to the opening of the mines, and the cultivation of the growth of the soil; and while at the same time the productiveness of the country is diminished, and the objects produced are rendered less productive to the population, the earnings of the laborer, and the value of labor, undergo a corresponding change.

There is no object to which the industry of a community is directed, which is not immediately affected by an augmentation of the charge for the transportation of the products of their toil.

They, in this vicinity, who desire to see an exemplification of these things, need only trace the proposed line of the James River improvement, and note the mountains which nature has charged with iron, and the furnaces at their bases idle. If they inquire the cause, they will find that without one single exception, it is that it costs too much to send the metal to market.

SECTION III.

OF THE EFFECT OF A CHANGE IN THE LENGTH OF AN IMPROVEMENT.

176. In the location of a line of improvement the question not unfrequently arises, to determine, in the choice of two routes of different lengths, that upon which the work should be established. And I believe it is usual in such cases, to allow the question to turn, for the most part, on the present cost of construction, and future maintenance, without allowing to the consideration of the increase or diminution of trade, and cost of transportation, any definite value.

A correct examination of the influence of such changes, will show that the question is much more extensive, and frequently more complicated ; and that when the cost of the two lines is correctly estimated, and the consumption of time and the probable charge for repairs arising from the transportation upon each, are duly weighed, the most important quantities remain still to be considered.

Every change of the length of an established line of improvement, will be productive of a corresponding change of the quantity of freight which it will convey, of the charges which should be levied, and of the revenue which will be received from the tonnage.

177. Though we limit the investigation here to the question of an alteration of the length of the line, with reference only to the trade that comes upon its further extremity, the results will be equally applicable to that which reaches it at any other positions.

We have already seen, when an improvement between the Atlantic and western waters is in competition with the navigation of those streams, what the value of the tonnage will be, for the exports and imports of the west, in the supposition that the work is conducted most profitably; and it is evident at once, by an inspection of equation (30), that a diminution of the length h, the quantity h' would produce a change in the expression of the quantity of freight, represented by

$$t\,(x' - x) = t\,\frac{h'\,\delta}{4\,\pi}\;; \qquad (47)$$

or, *the tonnage will be increased by any reduction of the length of the line an amount equal to the trade furnished by a portion of the Ohio valley, represented by the distance the length of the line is diminished, multiplied by the charge for freight on the improvement, and divided by four times the cost of freight on the river.*

178. The application of this formula to the trade on the Ohio, will give for the increase due to the saving of one mile of distance, on any canal connecting that river with tide-water,

$$t\,(x' - x) = 83\tfrac{1}{3} \text{ tons};$$

and the application being made in the same manner to a rail road, would give the double of this quantity, or 166⅔ tons.

179. If we make the substitution of $h - h'$ for h in equation (28), which expresses the toll that should be charged on the trade of the lower Ohio, we shall obtain

$$C + c = \frac{X \pi - (h - h') \delta + M}{2 (h - h')},$$

for the new value of the profit that should be received per ton per mile. If from the latter quantity we deduct that given in the equation, we shall find for the positive increment of toll corresponding with the diminution h' of the length of the line,

$$c = \left(C + \frac{\delta}{2} \right) \frac{h'}{h - h'}. \qquad (48)$$

Where the change in the length of the line is small in comparison with the line itself—or, in general, where the variation is not more than one tenth the distance represented by h, we may write this equation simply

$$c = \left(C + \frac{\delta}{2} \right) \frac{h'}{h}. \qquad (49)$$

We learn from equation (48), that *if the length of the line be curtailed, the charge for toll should be augmented a quantity ascertained by multiplying the former toll*

added to half the freight, by the ratio of the variation
of the distance to the length of the shortened line.

180. The fact that this formula will exhibit very small
variations of toll, for very small differences of distances,
does not militate against the truth of the principles involved in the discussion. Nor does it render the propriety of purchasing a decrease of distance by an increased outlay for construction at all questionable. In
general, there will be a sufficient number of points at
which the question of the proper route to be selected will
occur, to render the variation of the charge due to their
assembled length quite perceptible. And, withal, if any
portion of the trade continue to pass without any change
of the price of toll, the increased tonnage will, as we
have seen, when the toll is properly regulated, nearly
compensate for the omission.

181. There yet remains for discussion the important
problem, to determine to what extent the location should
be influenced, to obtain the increase of toll and tonnage
which has been shown to have place under any diminution of the length of the line; or, in other words, to determine what additional outlay should be permitted for
the purpose of constructing the shorter of two lines.

We will observe, by reference to equation (31), that
where we suppose h to become $h - h'$, the expression of
the aggregate dividend due to that portion of the western
trade obtained from the Ohio below the position at which
the improvement joins the river, will change to that of

$$t \frac{(\, \mathrm{X} \, \pi - (\, h - h' \,) \, \delta + \mathrm{M} \,)^2}{8 \, \pi}.$$

By deducting the first of these expressions from the second, and reducing, we shall obtain for the increase sought, of the aggregate revenue of the whole line,

$$\mathrm{R} - \mathrm{R} = \left(t \, \frac{\mathrm{X} \, \pi - h \, \delta + \mathrm{M}}{4 \, \pi} + t \, \frac{h' \, \delta}{8 \, \pi} \right) \delta \, h'; \quad (50)$$

an expression which indicates that *the increase of revenue caused by a reduction of the length of the line, is that due to the arithmetical mean between the tonnage before and after the reduction, carried over the space which it is proposed to diminish the length of the line, at the price for freight charged on the work.*

182. When this reduction of distance is not very considerable, we may neglect the increase of tonnage forming the second factor of the above equation, and, calling T the whole tonnage of the improvement, write in place of the preceding expression,

$$\mathrm{R}' - \mathrm{R} = \mathrm{T} \, h' \, \delta \, ; \quad (51)$$

or, *the augmentation of the revenue, in consequence of the diminution of the distance, is equal to the actual cost of transporting the whole tonnage of the improvement over the distance proposed to be saved ;*—a result perfectly in accordance with the general fact, which is obvious without the aid of any investigation, that *the revenue will always be increased at least as much as the expense of carriage is diminished;* and this property is coexistent with the decrease of the whole tax, and the augmentation of tonnage and toll shown to have place by equations (47) and (48).

183. This conclusion is equally applicable to the trade obtained from any branch connecting the improvement with a rival; whether it come in at the termination of the work, or at any other point along the line beyond the limit of the application of the principles discussed in Section 10, Part I, of this volume.

And if we perform the same operation on the expression of the revenue derived from a branch which forms no connection with a rival, and in respect to those articles which can sustain but a limited charge for carriage, we shall arrive at a result which may be announced in precisely the same language.

184. It is easy for us to perceive that an increase of the length of an improvement would be productive of a loss to the owner, or consumer of the property transported the additional distance. But that the company who are the proprietors of a canal, and who receive a certain toll for the use of the increased distance, should likewise be losers to this same amount, would appear (from the circumstance that the truth is not generally recognized) not to be so obvious; but it is a fact which results from the diminu-

tion of the trade, and of the toll, which is shown to be a function of the trade.*

185. The importance of this result is too great to be overlooked in the establishment of the line of an improvement; for the engineer who suffers his work to have a length only one mile greater than is necessary, not only entails on the community the burthen of the charge for transporting the whole trade that unnecessary distance, and shuts out a considerable amount of tonnage, but he deprives the company, whose work he constructs, of receipts more than equal to the tax with which he loads the public.

For the sake of an application of equation 51, we will suppose the question of the propriety of a change of location to arise in the progress of the enlargement of the Erie canal, by which it is proposed to save one mile of distance.

The tonnage towards the eastern end of that line may be safely assumed at one million five hundred thousand tons, on the completion of the work of enlargement; and, if the estimates of the advocates of the unusual dimensions which have been adopted by the

---

* If the author be thought to dwell too much on a fact so apparent, he will claim indulgence on the ground that this simple truth is not usually acknowledged, and, when comprehended, is not always fully appreciated. He has met with some difficulty in his practice in attempting to give the consideration its proper value.

commissioners, be correct, the average charge for freight—
all expenses included—will not exceed six mills per
ton per mile.

With these data we shall have

$$R' - R = \$9,000 \; ;$$

or, the saving to the commonwealth of New York, caused
by a reduction of only one mile of distance, will be equal
to nine thousand dollars per annum. And for the purpose of making sure of this revenue, that state would
find it judicious economy to reduce the length of her
canal, wherever it can be effected at an increased expense of \$150,000 per mile.

186. In looking over the last report of the canal commissioners of New York, the writer cannot perceive from
the statement of the proposed alterations cited there, and
a comparison of the relative cost of the new and old
lines, that it is their practice to pay any considerable sum
for a diminution of distance.

Of the instances mentioned in the document in which
a change of location is made, several are supported by
the fact that the shorter line will be the cheaper ; and
the one for which the greatest outlay appears to be authorized, is that in the neighborhood of the Chittenango
landing, rendered necessary by other considerations than
the mere diminution of distance. At this place, the increased cost encountered is at the rate of about eighteen
thousand dollars per mile for a distance of less than

half a mile ; or only about the one tenth part of that
which, by the principle here contended for, should be
incurred, if necessary.

It may be, that there were no cases where an increase
of expenditure would permit a shorter and equally favorable line to be obtained ; and it may be, that the consideration of the fact that the value of property would in
some cases be disturbed to an extent that would render a
change unjustifiable, had to be regarded in establishing
the new line. But, it ought not to be forgotten, that
THAT is a work that will exist as long as the political
history of the great commonwealth of which it is the
highest glory, and that the burthens which are placed on
its trade now, will have to be sustained by posterity for
ages to come.

187. In the ordinary practice of the engineer, however, it would not be proper to assume for the tonnage of
the work the amount which it might be expected to attain
at some distant period. To do so, would be to tax the
constructors of the improvement with a charge, in the
advantages resulting from which they could not participate ;—to burthen the present for the exclusive benefit of
the future.

The individual enterprise which is directed to the improvement of the country, is no other than the desire of
gain—and the object should be kept consistently in view.

It would have been injudicious in the extreme, for the
constructors of the Erie canal to take for the basis

of their comparative estimates the present trade of that
work; for the trade was then still to be created, and the
interest on the additional expenditure would have been
accumulating until this time without any corresponding
benefit.

But the state is now in a different position—more than
half the trade is on the line, and the balance will be
there by the time the work is consummated. The outlay
may be made this year, and one half the interest on the
capital will be returned the next.

188. The fact that the state of New York will not
probably deem it expedient to keep up the toll to the
point which will yield the greatest revenue—a condition
essential to the obtaining of the full amount of this advantage,—is no reason why the change should not be
effected at the cost indicated. The fact, if it be one,
only goes to prove that the state values the increased
tonnage at a higher sum than the increased revenue.

189. In general, it is the belief of the stockholder, that
the work in which he has invested his funds, will yield,
soon after its construction, the legal interest of the capital involved. When this condition has place, the tonnage necessary to pay such a dividend should be assumed
in the estimate. Unfortunately, the cases are rare in
which a higher number might be confidently taken.

For the James River and Kanawha improvement, I
have already shown, Art. 116, that the company may
safely count, when their work is fairly in operation, on a

trade of more than 100,000 tons per annum for the
western end of their line. I can show, by abundant
proof, that an additional trade of 50,000 tons may be
securely anticipated, without looking to the additional tributaries contemplated along the line, for the average tonnage east of the Alleghany.

With these facts, we shall have for the annual revenue
due to the diminution of one mile of the length of the
canal, Art. 182,

$$R' - R = \$1875 ;$$

a sum equivalent to a capital of \$31,250. And in the
selection of a route, in the survey I am now conducting
for the continuation of the line to the Ohio, I have employed this sum for the measure of the value of distances saved.*

The application being made to the rail road from Covington to Kanawha, will give

$$R' - R = \$2500 \text{ per annum } ;$$

---

* In general applications of these formulæ, it would frequently be preferable to keep the constant and variable charges for
freight separate. The value of δ is the cost of carrying one ton
one mile ; and to the sum which expresses the importance of
saving one mile of distance, we have yet to add that portion of
the cost of its maintenance, which is independent of the amount
of trade, to arrive at the true value of such a reduction of distance.

a sum equivalent to an expenditure of $41,666$\frac{6.9}{100}$; and this is the value I have employed, where distance is at issue on the rail road.

190. In a line composed in part of rail road and partly of canal, or some other system, the question frequently arises to determine where the one should terminate and the other commence—where the connection should be formed between the lines.

If, in this case, we put h' for the distance between the two proposed points by the rail road, and h the distance between them by the canal—a distinction which it is proper to make, since the lengths of the two works in the distance at issue might differ—and δ' for the freight on the rail road, and δ for that on the canal, we shall have, evidently, from equation (51),

$$T (h' \delta' - h \delta) \qquad (52)$$

for the annual difference of revenue in the two cases, where the whole space at issue is short.

191. When h becomes equal to h', the value of this equation will be changed to

$$T h' (\delta' - \delta). \qquad (53)$$

That the loss of revenue should be nothing, equation (52) should evidently become

$$h' \delta' - h \delta = 0,$$

and, consequently, we have the condition

$$\frac{h}{h'} = \frac{\delta'}{\delta}.$$

But by the rates we have assumed $\dfrac{\delta'}{\delta} = 2$; and conse-

quently, *it will generally be best,* CÆTERIS PARIBUS, *to carry on the canal in place of the rail road, unless one half the distance at issue can be saved by the substitution of the latter.*

192. For the purpose of an application of these formulæ, we will take the question so frequently discussed among the friends of the James River and Kanawha line, of the proper point to terminate their canal and commence the rail road. By some, the town of Buchanan would be preferred, while the company have adopted, by a resolution of the first meeting of the stockholders, that of Covington.

The distance between these two places, by the canal, is about 45 miles ; and if we assume for the tonnage 125,000 tons* we shall obtain, equation (53,)

$$T\, h'\, (\delta' - \delta) = \$70,312$$

for the annual loss of revenue. Or, the loss to the company by such a change of their plan, when their trade shall have attained 125,000 tons, and making a liberal allowance for a reduction of the charge for freight on rail roads to be anticipated from future improvements, would exceed the interest of a capital of more than one

---

* One hundred thousand tons being the estimated value of the Ohio trade, we may safely assume an increase of twenty-five thousand for the portion of the line west of Buchanan.

million of dollars.　But it would, in fact, be greater than this, as has been demonstrated in Art. 181.

193. If the distance at issue were *one foot*, instead of 45 miles, as above, the application of the principles will show that the substitution of a rail road for a canal, for that one foot, will subject the company to an annual loss of about thirty cents on the one hundred and twenty-five thousand tons supposed to be conveyed—and that it would be better for them to pay down *five dollars* than permit the substitution to be made.

We are not, however, to forget, in the application of these formulæ, the exception in favor of the case in which the charge for toll is limited by legal restrictions, to which we have adverted in Section 10, Part I.

SECTION IV.

OF THE EFFECT OF CHANGES IN THE RELATIVE AD-VANTAGES OF MARKETS.

194. The formulæ already obtained, may be applied directly for the determination of any fact connected with this subject. But there are some views which may be more distinctly exhibited by easy transformations, that will perhaps render more evident the importance of this subject to the success of the improvement by which the market is sustained.

If in any of the forms for the expression of the toll producing a maximum revenue, as that of equation (28), referring to the trade of the lower Ohio, we suppose M to be augmented by the increment m, representing any permanent improvement of the market at which the line is supposed to terminate, over that to which the trade is conducted by the rival, we shall have

$$C' = \frac{X\pi - h\delta + M + m}{2h},$$

for the new toll which should be established.

Deducting equation (28) from this second value of the charge for toll, we obtain

$$C' - C = \frac{m}{2h}, \qquad (54)$$

for the amount that the toll per ton per mile should be increased in consequence of the increased value of the commodity at the port to which it is sent.

If we make the change in the value of the market $1 00, and apply the formula to the James River and Kanawha improvement, we shall obtain $C' - C = \frac{10}{93}$ of a cent; or *an increase of one dollar in the Richmond market, will increase the toll on the James River and Kanawha improvement a little over one mill per ton per mile.*

195. If we use the form, equation (8), applicable to commodities which will bear but a limited charge, and

observe that the increase m is here analogous to an increase of the charge Π which the article will bear, we will remark that the results for the two cases are nearly identical. If the change of the value of the market be the consequence of its improvement, and not of the decrease of value of its rival, they are strictly identical.

196. We perceive, then, that the toll on all articles ought to receive an increase proportional to that of the price at the market it finds by being transported on the work; and that *the increase of charge per mile for toll that ought to be made, may be found by dividing the increase of the relative value of the article at the market on the line, by twice the distance it is transported on the improvement.*

197. For an additional example, let us suppose that from any cause the difference in the value of tobacco at Philadelphia and New Orleans should become half a cent per pound, or $11 20 per ton greater, in favor of Philadelphia this year than it was the last; we will have for the increased charge for toll proper to be made in this case,

$$C' - C = 1.4 \text{ cents per ton per mile.}$$

An increase of half a cent per pound in the comparative value of the article, would authorize an increase of one cent and four mills per ton per mile in the charge for toll.

By similar reasoning, we may demonstrate that the

whole tax on the commodity would be just as much increased as the toll is increased.

198. The same method applied to the expression of the tonnage will show that the increase of its value which will take place when M becomes M + m, will be

$$t\,(x' - x) = \frac{t\,m}{4\,\pi}. \qquad (55)$$

The value of this quantity is directly proportional to the change in the relative advantages of the two markets, and would amount, in the case of the preceding example, to the whole quantity of the trade found in a space along the tributary represented by

$$x' - x = 373\tfrac{1}{3} \text{ miles.}$$

199. The expression of the aggregate revenue on the improvement derived from all the trade transported from the Ohio, will be obtained by multiplying equation (31) by the length of the line.

And by substituting M + m in place of M, and deducting equation (31) from its new value, we shall find for the increase of revenue, on the whole work attributable to the change in the market,

$$\text{R}' - \text{R} = \left(t\,\frac{\text{X}\,\pi - h\,\delta + \text{M}}{4\,\pi} + t\,\frac{m}{8\,\pi}\right) m\,; \quad (56)$$

an expression obviously equivalent to the conclusion, that *the revenue will be augmented by any increase of the market, an amount obtained by multiplying the original tonnage added to half the increase of tonnage consequent on the improvement of the market, by the increased value of the tonnage, at the market.*

200. When the increase of tonnage is small in comparison with the whole original trade, we may neglect the second member of the preceding expression, and say, simply, that the value of the effect of the change is represented by the quantity

$$\mathrm{T}\,m\,; \qquad\qquad (57)$$

or, if the value of a market at the termination of an improvement, receive any small increase, while that of its rivals remains stationary, the improvement will obtain an accession of revenue, equal to the whole of the increased difference between the price for which all the articles brought by it from the west will sell at the market, and that at which they would sell at rival ports,—and to the increased difference betwen the whole cost of the articles bought there for the supply of the west, and what would be their cost if purchased at the rival mart.

In other words, *the increase of revenue consequent on the improvement of the relative standing of the market, is equal to the whole tonnage sent to, or taken from the port at which the work terminates, multiplied by the change in the relative prices of the commodities constituting the tonnage at that port and at its rival.*

A similar operation made with reference to the trade along the line of the work, which will bear but a limited charge, will conduct to the same result.

It may be readily shown, that if the tolls are properly adjusted at first, the increase of revenue represented by equation (57) will be caused by the improvement of the market, without any modification whatever of the charges.

201. We will not fail, then, to perceive the importance to the proprietors of the work leading the produce of the interior to any sea-port, of every change in the mercantile interests of the population of the place. Their interests are reciprocal and common, and most intimately connected in every department. A change cannot be made in the arrangement and plan of the improvement, which will not immediately affect the commercial prosperity of the port; and no change can have place in the value of the market at the port, which will not instantly tell back again upon the improvement.

An increase of price on a commodity at the market of an improvement, while it remains constant at that of a rival line, will at once produce an increased supply, and authorize an increase of charge—and through the influence of both considerations effect a change, of which the amount will depend on the change in the price, in the revenue derived from the trade.

202. It is not intended to convey the idea, that the charges on a line must vary with every fluctuation of the advantages of the markets. The tolls are established from time to time, and are regulated—or ought to be regulated—with a view to the permanent changes that

are produced in the circumstances that influence the condition and value of the improvement.

The work obtains the benefit of the transitory fluctuations by the increase of tonnage brought upon it; though the effect is frequently diminished by the increased charges for freight, on canals, which the carriers are enabled to levy, by taking advantage of the sudden demand for transportation. These do not interfere, however, with the permanent changes to which the principles here advocated are designed to apply; since the increasing competition will be commensurate with the increasing trade, and will prevent any permanent increase of taxation. Indeed, the opposite effect usually has place.

203. Such a change as we advert to, is that which would be produced by the growth of the city at which the demand for the article is supposed to exist: the augmentation of the demand arising from the increase of capital, and extension of the commercial connections of the population of the place, to lead to which the improvement is made. Such a change would be the value of any improvement of the harbor which would admit the shipping to the port more conveniently, and thereby reduce the cost of exportation.

204. The importance of this subject was adverted to, in a report of the writer on the consequences that would result to the city of Richmond and the James River and Kanawha Company, of diminishing the risk and inconvenience of communicating with the shipping,

on the presentation of a plan of a ship canal from Richmond to Warwick.*

He showed in that report, that a canal only four and a half miles long, passing the whole distance over level meadows, with scarcely a pebble to interfere with its construction, and requiring but four culverts, two locks and a dam across James River, would enable the company to bring ships of 600 tons burthen up to the wharves of Richmond, and into the very heart of the city. That the adoption of the plan would enable the merchant to avoid the delay, inconvenience, risk of damage, and frequent loss of property, resulting from the method practised of transmitting the lading of ships 60 miles by lighters, and loading in the river. That it would prevent, by bringing the canal boats and vessels together in the same basin, the expense of the unnecessary handling of freight in carting it to the lighters, and all the charges to which it would be subjected in the operation.

---

* This project was the result of a call made on the writer in his capacity of chief engineer, by the board of directors of the James River and Kanawha Company, to report on the most suitable plan for connecting the lower level of their canal at Richmond with tide-water. The plan was approved by the directors in the autumn of 1836, and adopted by the stockholders at their second annual meeting.

The application of the company to the Legislature for the extension of their corporate powers necessary to carry the scheme into effect, was unsuccessful.

Without repeating here the arguments in favor of the project, let us suppose the James River and Kanawha improvement completed, and passing on its line a trade of 150,000 tons of merchandise per annum ; and further, that the value of this improved connection with tide-water, was found to be equal to a saving of five cents per barrel on flour, or, generally, 50 cents per ton for all articles transported upon it.

Applying the rule to these quantities, we will obtain for the lowest limit of the increase of revenue on the James River and Kanawha improvement, in consequence of the construction of that work,

$$T \, m = \$75,000$$

per annum.

The augmentation of the company's revenue due to the consummation of this enterprise would, then, in this case, be equal to a capital of one million two hundred and fifty thousand dollars (without considering at all the toll on the ship canal itself)—a sum much more than sufficient to make the improvement.

205. It should be observed, that the conclusions here obtained, are always to be regarded as considerably below what ought to be anticipated in practice. The investigation reaches only the effects produced by the increase of trade, attributable to the increased space over which the influence of the work would extend, in consequence of the modification of the advantages offered by the line

and its port; but has no reference to the increased production consequent on the additional stimulus to labor, and the increased activity of trade which would be perceived in the districts previously using the improvement, on the occurrence of changes which would add to the gains of enterprise.

206. To the southern states engaged in the construction of works of this description, these considerations are in the highest degree interesting. Furnishing, as these states do, much the greater part of all the exports of the country, and transmitting their productions indirectly to Europe, and receiving their supplies by the way of northern cities, and through the hands, and by the aid of the credit of northern importers, the profits of their exports are subjected to excessive charges, and the cost of their supplies is enhanced by the profits obtained by the direct importer, through whom they are received.

The market situated at the termination of an improvement, through which both the imports and exports of any considerable portion of the south would be transmitted, must inevitably be increased in value by the concentration of trade, and consequent accumulation of capital, at that point. And as the age of the improvement increases, the change, at first partial, of the present mode of transacting business, would become more general in consequence of the increased regularity and amount of trade, and the confirmed reputation of the growing mercantile credit of the place.

Where the credit and capital exist, the demand will necessarily be found—and the demand gives value to the market: and it is thus that the improvement first creates the market, by bringing the commodities needed for exportation, as it creates the trade, and increases production, by offering an outlet for the products. And it is thus that the market which it creates, in its turn, reciprocates the act by offering inducements to the producer, to make use of the advantages afforded by the improvement.

But without engaging in the discussion of a semi-political subject, let us suppose the Charleston and Cincinnati rail road to be completed; that after it is fairly in operation, the trade has settled down to something like regularity, and that in this condition there are annually transported on it 25,000 tons of cotton.

If we assume that, from the causes adverted to, or any other, the value of cotton obtain an increase of $\frac{1}{4}$ of a cent per pound at Charleston, while no such increase is experienced at the other rival ports at which it is received and shipped,—then, I say, that the Charleston and Cincinnati rail road will receive an accession of revenue from this increased value of the market at Charleston, exceeding 20,000 tons, or 4,480,000 pounds of cotton at $\frac{1}{4}$ cent per pound—*exceeding one hundred and twelve thousand dollars per annum.*

207. The interest of this branch of our subject is augmented by the revolution that is opening upon us in the successful application of steam on the ocean; a revo-

lution that cannot be limited to the vessels employed in transporting the curious to Europe, but which is destined to supersede the uncertainty of the ancient method in almost every department of navigation. Wherever coal can be furnished, the steam ship will penetrate; and the trade of Europe, China, and South America will probably be conducted to our ports by this agent. The coal-mines and the machine shops will be the first to feel the impulse; but it is the sea-ports, situated high up our rivers, whose prosperity will be the most sensibly and permanently affected by it. The difficulty which the craft now navigating the ocean, experience in ascending to Philadelphia, Washington, and Richmond, will be reduced, and the relative importance of the latter will be increased.

In accordance with the principles here laid down, the public works leading the produce of the interior to these ports, will be benefitted by such a change, an amount equal to the increase of the relative value of the harbors at which they terminate, for all the tonnage passed through the improvements.

SECTION V.

OF THE EFFECT OF IRREGULARITY IN THE DISTRIBUTION OF TRADE.

208. The law assumed for the distribution of tonnage along the branches which supply the work, is undoubt-

edly that which the mind is at the first blush disposed to adopt. It is, withal, exceedingly well adapted to the nature of the investigation we have had in progress, since it is plain that the results must conform near enough to the actual state of things, to enable us to judge of the influence which particular variations in the conditions would be likely to produce.

But when we reflect that there must be much difference between the quantities of produce thrown upon the line, in different spaces of equal lengths; that one town will yield greatly more than another, and one river pour into its principal twice as much as the river adjacent to it; we may be justified in doubting, on a superficial investigation, whether the charges deduced under our supposition for those which will produce the greatest possible revenue, are really to be sufficiently depended on to guide us in practice.

In addition, we are aware that divers articles of trade are not to be met with at all in certain portions of the tributary furnishing the tonnage, and that many are but sparsely scattered in some places, and profusely spread in others.

The cotton of the Ohio and Mississippi are not met with for some hundred miles below the mouth of the Kanawha, and we must proceed a considerable distance down the Ohio from Pittsburg, before we reach the tobacco.

209. To examine this subject, we will suppose that in

a space of some miles between the point where the improvement meets the Ohio, and that where the direction of the trade changes—a space which we will represent by x'—the tonnage received per mile is t'; and that, with the exception of this distance, the valley would afford of the same article the quantity per mile represented by t.

We have already seen, that the distance to the point where the trade is divided is, by equation (22),

$$x = \frac{X \pi - h \epsilon + M}{2 \pi} ;$$

and the tonnage, consequently, which will reach the improvement under the charge ϵ, will be represented by

$$t \left(\frac{X \pi - h \epsilon + M}{2 \pi} - x' \right) + x' t' ;$$

and if we multiply this quantity by the company's toll per ton per mile, we shall obtain for the expression of the revenue per mile which would be derived from its transportation on the improvement,

$$r = t c \left(\frac{X \pi - h \epsilon + M}{2 \pi} - x' \right) + c x' t'.$$

The most advantageous charge for the use of the improvement, under the present condition, is that which will render this value of r a maximum.

By performing the operation, we obtain for its expression the equation

$$C' = \frac{X\,\pi - h\ \delta + M}{2\,h} + \frac{t' - t}{t}\ \frac{x'}{h}\ \pi. \quad (58)$$

210. If from the above quantity we deduct the value of C, under the supposition of an uniform distribution, we shall obtain for the difference of charge caused by the inequality of the trade,

$$C' - C = \frac{t' - t}{t}\ \frac{x'}{h'}\ \pi. \quad (59)$$

If, in this expression, we make $t' = 0$, which will correspond with the supposition that there is not any of the article obtained from the space x', we shall reduce the above equation to that of

$$C' - C = -\ \frac{x'}{h}\ \pi\,; \quad (60)$$

expressions which show that the toll will be less when the tonnage increases as we pass from the terminus of the work along the tributary which supplies the trade.

From equation (60), we may conclude that *when we do not meet with the commodity immediately on leaving the work and pursuing the tributary, the toll given by the condition of an equal distribution, must be diminished an amount represented by the cost of transportation on the branch, multiplied by the ratio of the distance from the work at which the article is first encountered, to the length of the improvement.*

211. For an example of this conclusion, we will suppose that we do not meet with any given commodity of western growth on leaving the James River and Kanawha line, until we have proceeded 80 miles down the Ohio ; and that we find it from that point onward, distributed in equal quantities in equal distances.

In this case, we shall have for the variation which the toll should experience in consequence of a total deficiency of trade, in the space of 80 miles next to the improvement,

$$C - C' = \tfrac{1}{8} \text{ of a cent per ton per mile.}$$

But we have already seen, that an error of one mill in establishing the most advantageous toll would probably produce a loss in the revenue on the principal articles of western commerce, of but about $\tfrac{1}{3}$ of one per cent.

212. To take another case, we will suppose that the tonnage per mile found in the first 200 miles below the mouth of the Kanawha, was discovered to be 300 tons per mile, and that beyond this distance it became uniformly 200 tons per mile. These numbers being substituted in equation (59), will produce an increase of

$$C' - C = \tfrac{5}{31} \text{ of a cent,}$$

or about $1\tfrac{3}{5}$ mills per ton per mile.

This second supposition is analogous in its effect to that of meeting with a city or river in the first two hundred miles, which would contribute an amount of trade equivalent to an increase of the whole tonnage of that distance, 50 per cent. above that of the other parts of the valley.

Now, there is in fact no such city or river—excepting the Mississippi,—on the whole line from Pittsburg to New Orleans; and any one at all familiar with the trade of that route, will allow that the departure from an equal distribution which we have here assumed, is high enough to satisfy us, that there will be no portion of the distance on the Ohio where a greater inequality over so large a space exists; and that, consequently, there will be no point where the article is found in the whole space between the improvement and the dividing line, that the toll deduced from the hypothesis of an uniform distribution, is likely to vary more than $1\frac{1}{2}$ mills per ton per mile from the most advantageous charge.

213. The applications which we have made of the facts supposed to exist show, therefore, that except in extreme cases, the difference between the charge that would be given under the uniform distribution, and that which ought really to be made, will not be sufficient to produce any essential variation in the revenue. And, at the same time, it is in our power to detect any remarkable irregularity in the productiveness of different sections of the country supplying the trade in any article, and so modify the charge given by the equations here offered, when the variation is sufficient to need it.

I do not, therefore, hesitate to say, that the trade approaches near enough to uniformity, to enable us, in all cases, to determine the toll which will render the work most productive.

214. They whose duty it is to fix the toll, should make the subject of the trade—the distribution of the tonnage—their study. And with a little application, they may learn to know on what portions of any given branch the several articles which it needs, or furnishes, are most abundant. And if it be found, that any of the varieties of objects are received in the greatest quantity from that portion of the branch nearest to the improvement, the toll, on those commodities, should be higher than that indicated by the formulæ, and the addition may be made by one of the preceding equations. If the quantity, however, seem to increase as we advance along the tributary, the toll, in order to satisfy precisely the condition of a maximum revenue, should be slightly diminished.

A very little general information concerning the distribution of trade, will enable the engineer to establish, with the greatest desirable accuracy, the precise charge that should be levied on each article of commerce. The corrections of the general formulæ which are given in this section, place it in his power to make use of any statistical information he may possess relating to the distribution of tonnage, and compensate, with all needful precision, for its inequality.

SECTION VI.

OF THE CONDITION OF THE PENNSYLVANIA IMPROVEMENTS.

215. The state of Pennsylvania, with the energy characteristic of her population, has embarked in a scheme of wide and ambitious improvement. Her lines spread over a great extent of territory, and embrace, in the object of their construction, both the trade of the distant west through the Ohio, and that of the north-west through the lakes.

The plan, though apparently imperfect, has been pursued with as much system as would seem to be compatible with the conflicting interests which are found to exercise an influence over popular representation. A line has been opened to the Ohio, and noble branches have been thrown off from it, which are every year extended farther towards their object.

There may be much to condemn in the system pursued, but there is more to praise in the enterprise which has sustained her efforts. For her works, though far less successful than a different policy might have made them, have done much for the internal commerce of the state, and have brought a considerable trade to her beautiful city, which, but for their existence, would have flowed to rival ports.

216. But, for these advantages, whatever they may be worth, she has paid at least the amount of her present debt on their account, or the sum of $22,229,000 ; has incurred the responsibility of a loan of that amount ; and independently of the cost of extending her line, is now annually paying for interest and the maintenance of her improvements, one million of dollars more than she receives in return from them.

I arrive at this conclusion, by assuming 5 per cent. for the interest on her loans ; which, on a capital of $22,229,000, will amount to the sum of $1,111,450.

By taking the aggregate length of her line of canals at 600 miles, and her rail road at 120 miles ; and assuming for the cost of superintendence and repairs of the former $800 per mile, and for the latter $2,000 per mile, we obtain for the charges on

600 miles of canal, at $800,	$480,000
120 do. of rail road at $2,000,	240,000

Making the aggregate cost of repairs, damages and superintendence,	-	-	$720,000
Adding interest on loans,	-	-	1,111,450
Produces for the annual charges,	-	-	$1,831,450

217. If this estimate be correct, the annual charge of keeping up those works, and paying all expenses incident thereto, together with the interest on the loans incurred for their construction and re-construction, will be *one million eight hundred and thirty-one thousand four hundred and fifty dollars.*

The revenue derived from the improvements, amounted the last year (1837), to $758,765, and the year before (1836), to $671,525.

The difference between these sums will show an increase for that year of $87,240.

The difference between the revenue for the years 1835 and 1836, was $73,893.

If we now deduct the last year's revenue from the estimated annual charges, we shall have an excess of expenses over the production of the work, equal to $1,072,685 per annum.

The interest on this sum at 6 per cent., is $64,367 ; differing less than twenty-three thousand dollars per annum from the annual increase of revenue drawn from the experience of the last year, and but about nine thousand five hundred dollars from that increase obtained from the experience of the year before.

It appears, then, that *the interest of one year's increase of debt is nearly equal to the annual increase of revenue ; and that there will consequently be a debt accumulating at the rate of more than one million per annum, unless the interest be kept down by the application of some other fund.* *

218. This result depends in part on the correctness of my estimate of the cost of maintaining the improvements, and in part on the estimate of the annual increase of revenue.

In regard to the former, I have only to say, that I think the past experience of the state will justify it ; that taking the two preceding years for a test, it will be found, if the subject be fairly analyzed, that the annual expenses have exceeded the sum of $700,000.

The experience of New York is, unfortunately, equally conclusive. On five of the principal canals of that state, having an aggregate length of 517 miles, the average cost of maintenance, for the year 1836, was $1,006 per mile, and for the next year $914 per mile.

These works are generally better constructed than

---

* This article was written during the author's passage through the line of the Pennsylvania improvement in the month of May. Since the work was sent to press, he has seen a statement of the actual result for the fiscal year 1838. It appears from this publication, that the aggregate toll, before deducting that for locomotive power, has amounted to $950,336, or about $25,000 *less than that of the previous year.*

This deficiency is doubtless chiefly attributable to the destruction of a portion of the main line in Huntingdon county—a circumstance that will be found considerably to enhance the charges of maintenance for the year.

those of Pennsylvania, and none of them are exposed to the violence of the floods of such streams as the Susquehanna and Alleghany, and their tributaries.

219. In stating the revenue for the last year at $758,765, it is intended to exclude the motive power tolls; and for the plain reason, that those tolls are merely adequate to the support of that power—and only reach the treasury, to be again drawn upon, for the purpose of defraying the expenses incident to its maintenance.

It may be thought, perhaps, that I have under-estimated the annual increase of revenue that ought to be expected from the works. The fact may possibly be true ; but if we have regard to the circumstance that the branch lines are yet incomplete, and that until finished they will be unproductive, we shall have reason to beleive, that the interest on the new debt that must be incurred for their extension, re-construction and repairs, will, until they are accomplished, be more than equivalent to any deficiency of the estimate of the probable future revenue.

I think, therefore, that I am fully authorized by the facts, in asserting, that the maintenance of the works of Pennsylvania are now increasing the state debt more than one million of dollars per annum.

220. I am aware that the sanguine and bold advocates of the system adopted by the state, hope for great returns on the extension of the North branch canal to the state line, the West branch to lake Erie, the Gettysburg

road to the Potomac, and the completion of the Sandy
and Beaver, and Mahoning connections. My expectations are, however, different.

The trade of the North branch will be exclusively limited to the produce of the country through which it
passes, which are utterly inadequate to its maintenance.

The extension of the West branch to lake Erie will
likewise command the trade of the country bordering the
line. But that which is floating upon the lake can pass
much more readily to New York even now, and will be
more perfectly secured to that city, on the completion of
the enlargement of the Erie canal, and the extension of
the Erie rail road, to the west.

The success of the Gettysburg extension is contingent
upon that of the Baltimore and Ohio rail road, which is
a competitor of the main line of the state; and the success of this work is therefore to some extent contingent
on the failure of that from Philadelphia and Pittsburg.

In fact, there is no source from which the commonwealth can look for an extraordinary revenue for the
expenditures made on account of her improvements.

Until the rival lines have approached more nearly their
completion, the tolls and tonnage will undoubtedly increase; but it will be only the regular progressive increase
arising from the growth of the country traversed by the
works, and that of a very limited circuit near the head of
the Ohio. There is no new trade to be thrown upon the
lines, and no new works to be opened, or old ones to be

extended, from which any considerable accession of revenue can be anticipated.   But all the intended new works
and extensions, will require new loans for their construction, and additional charges for their maintenance.

221. But there are other important considerations
which are likely to interfere with the successful issue of
this great experiment.

In the prosecution of these improvements, the chief part
of the expense has been encountered to bring the trade of
the Ohio and western Pennsylvania to Pittsburg, and to
deliver the trade of the lakes and the northern part of
the state on the Susquehanna.

It is here we find the most defective feature of the
system.   When this part of the design is accomplished,
and the means of delivering the productions of the north
and west on the Susquehanna, and at Pittsburg, is obtained, the trade is not secured to the state, or to the commercial emporium of the state.

The tonnage delivered at Pittsburg has yet the Alleghany to overcome by a most inadequate improvement,
before it can attain the waters of the Susquehanna ; and
when this trade, and that of the north and west, are brought
upon that noble river, it is yet in effect excluded from Philadelphia.   To reach the Delaware, it must either encounter the passage through the small locks of the Union canal,
or undergo an additional transshipment at Columbia, and
be again subjected to the cost of rail road transportation
to the Schuylkill.

Such is the condition of things now; and in the meantime, a canal is in progress from Columbia to tide-water, which will afford a more convenient passage to the trade that may be collected on the line to a rival city.

222. I am of opinion that these defects cannot be entirely corrected but by the opening of a continuous water communication, by the shortest practicable route, from the Ohio to Philadelphia. That to secure the trade of the west, and even of Pennsylvania, to that city, the obstructions adverted to must be removed from the line, and the charge for transportation must be reduced; and there is no means fully adequate to this object, but the opening of a good and capacious canal.

The cost of sending a ton of western merchandise from Pittsburg to Philadelphia, is at this time about $20. If the line were a canal, it would be but about 8 dollars— or two fifths of the present charge.

The produce of the west, which now seeks the city of New Orleans from the lower Ohio and Missouri, might, by such a reduction of the charge, be at once drawn to Pittsburg, and thence to Philadelphia. A reduction of $12 per ton would immediaiely change the direction of the whole trade of the Ohio, Missouri and Mississippi, down to the mouth of the Ohio, and render it tributary to the improvements and commercial capital of the state.

To effect this object successfully, the navigation of the Ohio above Portsmouth must be improved, a canal must be constructed across the mountains, and the Union and

Schuylkill canals must become the property of the commonwealth, and the narrow locks of the former be adequately enlarged.*

223. The expenditures required for the execution of this scheme would undoubtedly be great. But the Union canal stock would become extremely profitable, as soon as the line would admit the large boats navigating the Susquehanna and Juniata divisions; and the Schuylkill canal would, in a few years, if adequately improved, be the most crowded, and one of the most profitable lines of navigation in the world.

The trade upon it is now vast, and rapidly increasing; and when the canal across the Alleghany would place there all the products of the Ohio and Mississippi, above the mouth of the former; would concentrate upon it the whole of the exports of the states bordering the Ohio, and those of Pennsylvania herself, it would indeed be immense. There can be no doubt entertained of the

---

* It is possible greatly to reduce the expense of transportation on this route without constructing a canal across the Alleghany.

Improvements may be introduced in the general conduct of the line from Philadelphia to Pittsburg, by which trade may be brought from the mouth of the Ohio, or even St. Louis, for the sum which it now costs to bring it from Steubenville, Wheeling or Marietta; and by a simultaneous correction of the tariff of toll, the revenue derived from the public works, would be equal to their maintenance, and the payment of the interest on all the loans incurred for their construction.

profitableness of the capital invested, in pursuance of such a policy, in that work.

224. I am aware that difficulties, and perhaps impossibilities, in extending the canal from the Juniata to the Conemaugh will be anticipated by many; but happily modern experience has rendered it dangerous to pronounce impracticable any thing in art that cannot be directly proved to be so.

A little while ago the application of the steam engine to river navigation was deemed impossible; and there are now millions who can recollect when the present daily performance of the locomotive would, if predicted, have been regarded as a visionary speculation. In this very year the success of the attempt to apply the same agent to the navigation of the Atlantic, was regarded as more than dubious by many of science, and experience in the mechanic arts.   And now, I will venture to say, that the power which propels two of these vessels across the Atlantic,—the engines of the Liverpool and Great Western—if planted on the Conemaugh, would lift a supply of water to the summit level of the canal, adequate to compensate for any deficiency that will ever be experienced there.

225. Such is the mode in which, I think, the state of Pennsylvania may retrieve her error, command a due portion of the trade of the west, and render her works eminently successful. By pursuing the policy with well digested plans, and avoiding deviations, the object might be

accomplished in four years, and the trade of her line might be increased five fold.   Her designs would be fulfilled.

But it is worthy of some speculation to determine what policy will probably be pursued by that state.   I believe that the apprehension that the plan I suggest is impracticable, together with the influence possessed by the patrons of the branches which are yet incomplete, will be sufficient to prevent the expenditures upon the central line necessary to open the communication in question.   And such will probably continue to be the condition of things, until her present plans are carried through, and the state debts shall have reached some $40,000,000, and the interest on the loans and expenses of the works shall exceed the annual revenue by two millions of dollars.

By that time it will probably be acknowledged, that the policy of the state is unsound ; and the evidence will be drawn from the disappointment of the present expectations, and the direct tax levied for the maintenance of the system.

226. In the meantime, it is to be observed, there are rival works in course of construction to the Ohio, and to the Susquehanna, which will reach those waters before the state policy is consummated, and divide with the commonwealth the trade she is seeking.   The James River and Kanawha improvement, passing through the centre of Virginia, is one of these, which will in the course of a few years be completed, and form a junction with the Ohio 260 miles below Pittsburg.   The work will be

capacious, and avoid many of the greatest obstructions upon the present Pennsylvania line. It will have the advantage of a more genial climate, a lower summit, a better rail road, and a junction with the Ohio, below the worst part of its navigation; where the ice breaks up earlier in the spring, and closes later in the fall, and where the summer drought is less injurious.

It can be shown that when this line is opened, it will not only command the trade below Point Pleasant, but take the up river trade from a higher point than Pittsburg, to the extent that its market will authorize. And this effect will be experienced at the very time when the need of Pennsylvania is likely to be greatest; when a larger amount of unproductive capital will be expended, and the annual charges of her works will have increased.

It is from the effect of this improvement, in connection with the probable condition of the state at that time, that I look for the commencement of the system of operations which is the only practicable method of obtaining and preserving her trade. To this she will be forced by the accumulating expenses of the works, and the abstraction of the western products which she now receives.

The consummation of the Virginia enterprise, will force the opening of a continuous water line in Pennsylvania. And when that water line is opened, its influence will be felt in Virginia, in the loss of the trade which will be recovered by Pennsylvania. And the consequence of this result, I think, is equally obvious. Virginia, to regain the trade taken back by Pennsylvania, will be compelled to extend the steamboat navigation from the falls of Kanawha up to the Greenbrier, and her canal from Covington over the Alleghany, to the new termination of the steamboat navigation.

227. Which, at this time, will be the favored work, what the precise division of trade, it is not my intention to consider. I am confident that the progress of the west in improvement and wealth, and the progressive expansion of business over a million of square miles, will pour an amount of trade into the valley of the Mississippi and its tributaries, which will be more than adequate to sustain them both. And no one should regret to see them reciprocally urged by an elevated competition, and the effects of each other's enterprise, to pursue that policy which will have the most rapid and permanent influence in the development of their respective resources, and in diffusing the blessing of commercial prosperity over a wide area of the Union.

SECTION VII.

OF THE IMPROVEMENTS OF NEW YORK AND VIRGINIA, IN COMPETITION FOR THE WESTERN TRADE.

228. The state of New York has been more successful than Pennsylvania in her labors in the career of internal improvement; a fact that is chiefly attributable

to a happy selection of a system, in the beginning, and a tenacious adherence, in her progress, to the well digested plans with which she commenced. The example is worthy of reflection.

If, in lieu of the Erie canal there had been made a McAdam road, it would, doubtless, have been more popular with a certain party, in the day of its construction; but the cost of carriage on a ton of lumber from Buffalo to Albany, instead of four dollars, as it is now, would have been from forty to sixty dollars, or three times the value of the article in market; * and if it had been a rail road, it would have furnished better accommodations to the hundred or more thousands of passengers who annually traverse it, but would still have levied a ruinous tax on the trade by which now it is chiefly sustained.

The soundness of the policy which dictated the character of that improvement is there acknowledged, after some twelve or thirteen year's experience ; and the state which has been rendered by its success the first in the Union, is in the act of exhibiting her confidence in her system, by the expenditure of four times the original cost of the work in its enlargement.

The course of New York has been steady and bold, and the results are those which usually reward enterprise directed by such policy.

---

* More than half the tonnage of the New York canals consists of the produce of the forest.

The revenue of her line is a source of wealth to the state, and the benefits which it has diffused over the face of the country, are felt by every member of her society. A confidence has been formed in the correctness of her progress, which supersedes the necessity of ordinary appeals for the support of her citizens. Her statesmen are impelled by the strength of public opinion, and the magnitude of the gigantic scheme she has projected, is the evidence of its force.

229. Looking at the destiny of their state with the pride and enthusiam created by successful enterprise, her citizens count on witnessing results spring from her present exertions, commensurate with the greatness of her efforts: and it would be difficult to assign a limit to the anticipated influence of the present scheme, in promoting the prosperity of the state, and spreading out the emporium of her commerce.

The whole region traversed by the Ohio, Mississipppi and Missouri, seems popularly supposed to be within her control, and is appropriated, in anticipation, for the supply of her trade. This object is, however, sought for by other interests, and Virginia, Pennsylvania and Maryland are already competitors for its possession.

It is worthy our attention, while these states are in the act of expending SIXTY MILLIONS OF DOLLARS for the attainment of this prize, to know whether it be true, that the enlargement of the Erie canal is to have the effect of neutralizing their exertions.

230. In this volume it has been supposed, that the course of trade will depend on the cost of transportation, and the value of the commodity at the markets to which it may be sent. I propose to continue that method in the present examination.

For the trade of the Ohio to reach the city of New York, by the way of the Erie canal, it is necessary for it to traverse the state of Ohio, or Indiana, by some of the contemplated, or existing improvements, connecting that river with lake Erie. We will suppose, that it will take the route of the present canal, which terminates at Cleaveland, on the lake, and at Portsmouth, on the Ohio.

The distance from Portsmouth to Richmond, by the way of the James River and Kanawha improvement, and the Ohio river, is 555 miles; of which 178 miles is a continuous steamboat navigation, and 239 miles, a canal of large dimensions, which is connected with the former by a rail road $138\frac{3}{10}$ miles in length.

The distance by the other route is from

New York to Albany,	150	miles ;
Albany to Buffalo,	363	"
Buffalo to Cleaveland,	190	"
Cleaveland to Portsmouth,	309	"

Making the whole distance from New York to Portsmouth, 1012 miles—by a line that is five twelfths of the year closed by ice.

Is it probable, that during the period that this line is open to New York, produce will be carried from the Ohio a distance of more than one thousand miles, and be subjected to the charges for transshipment and forwarding, at four different cities, when it might be taken to Richmond in about half the distance, and for less than half the charges other than is due to the transportation? I think not.

231. The actual cost of sending freight from New York to Portsmouth, is $2,00 per 100 pounds, and the charges at Portsmouth are about 10 cents per 100 pounds,—making together $2\frac{1}{10}$ cents per pound. We cannot suppose that these sums will be reduced by competition, since they exist now, while the Pennsylvania improvement, and steamboats on the Ohio, offer all that is needed for the purpose. But we may presume that the enlargement of the Erie canal will have an influence, and it would be proper to take it into consideration.

It is supposed, by the canal commissioners of New York, that the accomplishment of their magnificent design, will reduce the charges on merchandise sent to the west, one cent per ton per mile.* We shall then

---

* Report for 1837—their estimate is 9 mills per ton of 2,000 pounds.

have, for the cost of sending one ton from New York to the Ohio, after the enlargement of that work,

Present freight on 2,240 pounds, a $2\frac{1}{10}$ cents, $47 04
Deduct the transportation for 363 miles, a 1 cent,   3 63

Will give for the *future charge* from New York to Portsmouth, $43 41 per ton.

I have elsewhere shown, that the whole freight on merchandise from Richmond to Portsmouth, will not exceed $17 00,* or will be not much more than one third part of the preceding sum, representing the probable charge from the same point to New York, on the completion of the enlargement of the Erie canal.

I am under the impression, however, that the charges to New York, may be reduced somewhat below the sum here given, by a reduction of the *toll* on the Ohio and the Erie canals. Supposing this reduction to be one cent per ton per mile, and that the other charges incident to the transportation are likewise diminished, it is possible, that the whole expense by that line may eventually be brought down to $35 00 per ton.

Though these facts appear to militate against the sup-

---

* See appendix—where the average charge from Richmond to Point Pleasant is estimated at $12 55. The freight to Portsmouth should not exceed this sum by more than $1 50. Adding $3 00 for *additional toll* on merchandise, on the James River and Kanawha line, we obtain the sum stated above, $17 00.

position, that any portion of the trade of the Ohio can pass to New York, I do not doubt that that city will continue to have a deep interest in this trade; that it will forward, as now, its merchandise, and to some extent receive the productions of the west in return; but the improvements of Pennsylvania and Virginia will be the medium of intercourse.

232. In the preceding comparison, Portsmouth is assumed for the point at which to exhibit the respective charges for transportation, in conducting the trade of the Ohio to the Atlantic, by the works of New York and Virginia; and the result shows, that the charges by the way of New York, on the completion of the Erie canal, will probably be more than twice as great as by the James River and Kanawha line.

We will now determine their relative merits, when Cleaveland, on lake Erie, is the point of comparison.

From Richmond to this place, the distance will be 864 miles; and from New York to the same point it is 703 miles.

The actual charges from Cleaveland to Portsmouth, including the charges at Portsmouth, is 75 cents per 100 pounds, or $16 80 per ton of merchandise.

We shall then have,

Charges from Richmond to Portsmouth,   - $17 00
Add charges from Portsmouth to Cleaveland,   16 80

Which produces $33 80, for the whole expense from Richmond to Cleaveland.

We had previously found for the

Charge from New York to Portsmouth,   - $43 41
Deduct charge from Celaveland to Portsmouth,   16 80

and we obtain $26 61 per ton, for the probable average charge from New York to Cleaveland, after the enlargement of the Erie canal.

We perceive, then, that while Virginia could trans-mit merchandise from Richmond to Portsmouth, for $26 40 per ton less than it could be forwarded to the same point from New York, the latter could forward it to Cleaveland, the opposite extremity of the Ohio canal, for only about $7 20 per ton less than the sum for which it will be carried to that place from Richmond. It is apparent, therefore, that the point of division of trade would be north of the centre of the state of Ohio ; and, indeed, that if the appropriation of the commerce of the west, were determined only by the consideration of the cost of carriage, the influence of New York would be confined exceedingly near to the southern coast of lake Erie.

But during the seven months that this line is open, it is to be presumed, that the superiority of the northern market will give it a preference, to a certain extent, in many varieties of trade ; and the division line will con-sequently be thrown further south, a distance dependant on the amount of that preference. For most articles, this superiority cannot exceed the value of the freight, and other charges from New York to Richmond. These may be estimated to average, on merchandise, $3 00 per ton—since for that amount, they may be sent by the way of Virginia without an appreciable difference in time. But even admitting that the goods are purchased in New York, and forwarded by the way of Richmond, to the country traversed by the Ohio canal, they would still be sent to a point further north than the centre of the state. And the produce exported from Ohio, not being compelled to encounter the charges for freight between Richmond and New York, would be attracted to the south from a still higher point.

233. We do not, however, need any argument to establish these facts, since the actual result of the competion of New York with the improvement of Pennsylvania, shows that a great part of the merchandise purchased in the emporium of the former, and intended for the valley of the Ohio and Mississippi, is at this time actually forwarded to Philadelphia, and transmitted by the way of Pittsburg, at a cost twice as great as would be found to have place through Virginia. A ton of merchandise can be forwarded from New York to Portsmouth by the way of Richmond on the completion of the James river and Kanawha improvement for $20; and the actual charge of sending it through Pennsylvania is about $40, or $1 80 per 100 pounds. Under this charge it now

takes the Pennsylvania route; and the difference between the cost by the way of Pennsylvania and Virginia, is more than equal to the present cost of transportation from the Ohio to lake Erie.

I say, then, that on the Ohio canal, more than half the width of the state will seek the eastern markets by means of the navigation of the river; and it remains only to see what will be the probable course of the trade found west of that work.

234. The Ohio stretches from Portsmouth nearly due west; the southern shore of the lakes continues parallel with it a short space to the west of Cleaveland, where it bends to the north, and returns again at the southern point of lake Michigan. The territory which is to supply the trade, is enclosed between the lakes and the river.

The cost of transportation on the Ohio is less than one cent per ton per mile, and that on the lakes is always from two to four cents; so that if the lakes and the Ohio were parallel, the trade of the belt of country between them lying beyond the Ohio canal, would, as we advance to the west, continue to proceed to the Ohio from points farther north than the centre line : and the distance north of that line, from which the trade would flow to the south, would increase, in consequence of the difference between the freights on the lakes and on the Ohio, the further we would advance to the west. But after reaching Indiana, the lakes become nearly inaccessible, excepting for the state of Michigan and the northern corners of Indiana and Illinois.

It must then be apparent, that the chances of New York for the trade of the western states, east of the Ohio canal, are greatly superior to her prospects for any part of it west of that line. Because, advancing to the west along the lake she is compelled to contend with a navigation doubly as expensive as that of the Ohio.

235. After the enlargement of the Erie canal, the cost of sending merchandise from New York to Chicago—if the tolls and freights on the Hudson and the lakes maintain their present value, and the freights on the canal be reduced one half—using steam on the Hudson, and vessels on the lakes,——will be

From New York to Buffalo,   - $0 70 per 100 lbs.
From Buffalo to Chicago,   - $0 75 "   "   "

Making from New York to Chicago, $1 45 per 100 lbs. or $32 50 per ton of 2240 lbs.

If the goods were carried in steamboats, on the lakes, the charge would be $1 70 per 100 pounds, or $38 08 per ton of 2240 lbs.

The charge on merchandise from any position near St. Louis, to Point Pleasant, is generally at this time, when the water is in good condition, not more than $10 per ton, and will hereafter be reduced by the improvement of the navigation. Assuming, however, $10 for the future charge, and adding that sum to the cost of carrying the same articles from Point Pleasant to Richmond, which for merchandise would be about $16—will give us for the whole tax between the mouth of Missouri and Richmond but $26 per ton, or $6 50 per ton below the sum which will be paid from Chicago to New York.

What claims, then, will New York have on the trade of the Missouri, when this difference exists between the cost of carriage from Chicago to New York, and St. Louis to Richmond—the former subject to the delay of schooners on the lakes, and the latter expedited by steam on the Ohio.

236. But we may make the issue more immediately applicable by comparing the charges from Galena to Richmond, with those from Chicago to New York.

Galena is but 405 miles above St. Louis; the navigation of the Mississippi up to that point will be equal, or better than that of the Ohio to Pittsburg; and the charges, whenever the trade acquires sufficient importance to produce much competition, will not be higher. At the price which I have stated for the future freight on the western waters—$\frac{3}{4}$ cents per ton per mile—the charge from Galena to Richmond will be $3 higher than from St. Louis to Richmond. Or, the cost of sending one ton of goods from Galena to Richmond will be $29, while we have seen that from Chicago to New York it is $32 50, and subject to the delay and uncertainty of traversing 900 miles of the northern lakes in common schooners. If the basis of the comparison were, as it ought to be, the charge by steamboats in both cases, the cost from Galena to Richmond, would be to that from Chicago to New York, as $29 is to $38—or about in the proportion of 3 to 4.

But Galena lies due west of lake Michigan, from which it is separated by 160 miles of land carriage. It lies, too, between New York and the trade of the north western territory—which must, I think, be forever excluded from a direct communication with that city, by the higher charges it will have to sustain in reaching it.

237. On the whole, while it must be admitted that the trade of Michigan will chiefly, and perhaps exclusively, pass to New York, the Southern half of Ohio, more than half of Indiana, nearly all of Illinois, and the whole of Missouri and the North Western territory, and the states south of the Ohio, will continue to seek the markets of New Orleans, Pennsylvania, Maryland, and Virginia.

Such will be the course of trade in the summer season, when the issue of the competition is tried on the merits of the routes, and the advantage of climate which the southern lines will possess over their northern rivals, has no influence on its direction. In the winter these will have the exclusive possession of the business.

The contemplated enlargement of the Erie canal will have no serious effect on the result. For even admitting the correctness of the computations of the canal commissioners, that the freight on that line will be reduced to one half its present value, or 5 mills per ton per mile, and

that the tolls continue as at this time, the enlargement
will effect a reduction of but $1 81½ per ton on the
whole charge for agricultural products—a sum quite inadequate to the purpose of drawing the trade from those
great districts of country.

Even if, after the reconstruction of that great work,
the charges for toll were entirely sunk, for the purpose of
reaching the trans-Mississippi trade, the object could not
be attained. The whole charge on heavy articles, for
toll and freight from Buffalo to Troy is but about $7 25
per ton—a sum barely exceeding the difference between
the tax on merchandise from Galena to Richmond, and
from Chicago to New York—the freight on the latter passage being by schooners.

238. The trade of the Erie Canal will continue to be
supplied from the great state of New York, and the immediate coast of the lakes. It cannot command any considerable portion of that beyond the Mississippi, and very
little of that south of the forty-first degree of latitude.
Nor, indeed, is it necessary for her influence to stretch
beyond these limits, to secure the most abundant return
for her labors in the career in which she has set out, and
obtain a trade worthy of the leading state of a great nation, and worthy of a capital that is soon to be abreast of
the greatest in the world.

She needs no false calculations; she requires not the
extravagant speculations of enthusiastic minds, to justify
the course she is pursuing, or give assurances of ultimate

success. She has in reality within her reach, and indeed in her possession, the commercial control of a country which may well satisfy the most ambitious spirit of appropriation. But her influence is limited by the physical geography of the country, and her legitimate field is well defined by its outlines.

Nature, in the formation of the great divisions of the Union, and its watercourses, would seem to have been averse to monopoly, and have meted off to each its appropriate trade.

To New York she has given the coast of the lakes, and the Hudson, and left it to her enterprise to form a connexion by a system worthy of the benefits to flow from the bond.

To New Orleans, the emporium of the south, is appropriated the Mississippi, with its thousand arms stretching to the confines of the most fertile territory on the continent.

To Virginia is assigned the Ohio, and Kanawha, and James rivers, forming a direct and almost continuous line, through a double column of productive territories, to its confluence with the Mississippi, where the trade of the vast region watered by the Missouri and that river, and their tributaries, will be concentrated and divided.

To Pennsylvania is granted a soil productive in vegetation, mountains charged with minerals, and a population possessing the enterprise capable of surmounting the physical obstacles in the way of her access to the products of the west. She shares, and, I doubt not, will continue to share them.

The value of the harvest to spring from the labors of all, is made to depend on the judicious application of the advantages which they respectively possess, and on the skill with which the object is sought.

APPENDIX.

JAMES RIVER AND KANAWHA IMPROVEMENT.

In the course of this volume, reference is frequently made to the James River and Kanawha improvement; and the examples used to illustrate the formulæ, are generally applied to that work. A few observations upon the enterprise will not therefore be inappropriate.

The company engaged in the construction of this line of public improvement, was incorporated by the legislature of Virginia, in the year 1832; but the conditions required by the acts of assembly, were not complied with until the spring of 1835, when the first general meeting of the stockholders was convened, and the company duly organized.

The object of the improvement is the connexion of James river, at Richmond, with the Ohio, at Point Pleasant. The plan by which it is intended to be accomplished, is a canal from Richmond to Covington, on Jackson's river, a rail road from Covington to the Kanawha, and an improvement of the channel of that stream to its confluence with the Ohio.

The fall of the Kanawha, from the point where it is reached

by the rail road, to its entrance into the Ohio, is rather greater than that of the Ohio above their junction. It is well adapted for improvement, and when improved, will present a navigation much superior to that of the Ohio, in its present state, though not as good as the latter is susceptible of being made.

It may be regarded as an extension to the east of the Ohio; since it will offer, for all purposes, nearly as cheap and easy a line of communication; and the steamboats which navigate that river, can ascend it at all times with their cargoes, without the necessity of transshipment.

The line of artificial construction is, therefore, the canal up James and Jackson's rivers to Covington, and the rail road from Covington to the Kanawha river.

The route of the rail road lies across the Alleghany, by the way of Dunlap's creek, Fork run, and Howard's creek, to Greenbrier river—which it crosses, and follows down to its junction with New river. The line of the road is placed on the north side of New river, where some of the principal difficulties in the way of its construction, are encountered.

DISTANCES.

The length of the line, from tide water to steamboat navigation, on the Kanawha, is $377\frac{1}{5}$ miles; of which $238\frac{35}{100}$ miles consists of canal, from Richmond to Covington, and $138\frac{3}{10}$ miles of rail road, from Covington to the Kanawha.

The distance from the termination of the rail road to the Ohio river, at the mouth of the Kanawha, is $87\frac{75}{100}$ miles.

The elevation of the canal at Covington
is . . . . . . 1229 feet above tide.

Highest summit of the rail road, being
the level of the tunnel through the
Alleghany mountain, . . 1987 " " "

Lowest summit of the mountain where
pierced by the tunnel, . . 2325 " " "

Kanawha river, at the foot of Loup
creek shoal, the western terminus of
the rail road, ... 608 " " "

Ohio river, at the mouth of the Great
Kanawha, ... 522 " " "

OF THE CANAL.

The general dimensions of the canal are a depth of 5 feet,
width at surface of 50 feet, and at bottom of 30 feet. The
banks usually rise two feet above the surface of the water.
Their width on the towing path side is 12 feet, and on the
berm side, generally 8 feet.

The first three miles next above Richmond is constructed on
a much larger scale—being 80 feet wide at surface, and 8 feet
deep. The object of this unusual size is to furnish a supply
of water, for hydraulic purposes, to the city of Richmond,
which it will deliver along the banks of James river, at an
elevation of about 80 feet above tide.

The construction of this portion of the line was a work of
great labor and heavy expense ; and in recommending the

unusual dimensions given to the work, the author endeavored to sustain his opinion on the ground that the expenses would not be very materially augmented by it, while the successful consummation of the enterprise in which the company were engaged, would secure a demand for all the power that could be supplied. His plan was approved and adopted by the directory, and the work has since been successfully accomplished.

There is now an average force of 3,500 men engaged on the FIRST DIVISION, of $147\frac{1}{2}$ miles above Richmond; and there is much reason to hope that the whole of this portion of the line will be opened to the public in the course of the year 1839.

The prism of the canal in this space is generally completed, and the erection of the works of art is progressing vigorously.

In the preparation of the plans of these works, it has been the primary object to reconcile the conflicting conditions of durability and economy, as far as was compatible with the nature of the subject. The aqueducts are of excellent massive stone, and are ornamented with little work that does not add to their stability. They afford a width of water way at the surface of 21 feet. The culverts are likewise built of substantial masonry, and with little extraneous ornament.

The original plan of the locks required them to be of cut stone, and fifteen have been erected after the first design. Considerations of economy have since led to the substitution of a less permanent structure.

In the location of the work, special caution has been observed to give to the consideration of distance the value indicated to be proper for it, in the annexed Essay. This circumstance has made it necessary frequently to carry the line across James and Jackson's rivers, above the Blue Ridge, and, in several instances, to encounter tunnels of considerable difficulty. The result consequent on the admission of this principle, has been to produce a location in the 230 miles between Lynchburg and Kanawha about 19 miles shorter than would have been obtained by adopting the cheapest route, and to increase the whole cost about $250,000.

PLAN OF THE RAIL ROAD.

In my report on the results of the examination for the route of the rail road, I have recommended,

I.   That the second track required by the charter, be, if permitted by the Legislature, dispensed with; and that the road bed be graded for a single track only :

II.   That the velocity for the transportation of heavy freight be reduced to 6½ miles per hour:

III.   That the width of the track be enlarged to 6 feet:

IV.   That a heavy class of engines—weighing from 15 to 25 tons—be employed in the transportation :

V.   That the warehouses be established by the company.

My report of the present year contains the arguments by which I have endeavored to sustain these recommendations. I will here repeat, in few words, some of the reasons which have prompted me to do so.

I. REASONS FOR SUPPRESSING THE SECOND TRACK.

I have endeavored to show, in the first part of this volume, the additional expense that must be incurred for the mainte-nance of the extra track of a rail road, from the Atlantic to the

Ohio. This expense is stated to be the interest on $18,000 per mile, and an annual charge for repairs of $500 per mile.

The length of the rail road, from Covington to the Kanawha river, is 138.3 miles ; and the additional cost of constructing a double track in a permanent style, over the cost of a single track, would be, in round numbers, $2,500,000 ;* and the additional cost of repairs, in its maintenance, at $500 per mile, would be $69,150. The interest on the extra capital required, added to the additional annual charges, would therefore amount to the sum of $219,150.

The whole length of the James River and Kanawha improvement, by the line proposed, will be 465 miles; and we have obtained for the probable average toll, on the western trade, one cent per ton per mile.

The profit on each ton carried across the line of the improvement would therefore be $4 65.

If we divide the annual charges due to the additional track by this sum, we shall find 47,129 tons, for the trade that must be passed entirely through the line from the Ohio to tide-water, to pay the interest on the capital invested in the additional track, and keep it in proper repair. This trade is equal to the whole tonnage of a space of some 200 miles of the valley of the Ohio, below Point Pleasant.

It has been my wish to relieve the company of this drawback on their profits, in proposing to suppress the portion of

---

*The entire cost of a road, with a single track, is estimated in my report at $2,425,950. This estimate refers to such a superstructure as ought to be at first made; the estimate above applies to the permanent road, by which it will eventually be superseded.

their labor by which it would be produced. The advantage to be derived from the measure is apparent, and the only question that need be considered in this place, is that of the sufficiency of the single way.

A continuous line of more than 114 miles of the rail road—extending from the western base of the Alleghany to the Kanawha river—will be constructed with maxima grades of 20 feet per mile. The part of the line where the grades are higher, embraces the mountain section, and a portion of the descent to Jackson's river. The grades exceeding 20 feet are all found in a space of 24 miles.

On ascending planes of 20 feet per mile, the heavy engines recommended will be able to draw, at a speed of 6½ miles per hour, gross loads of 400 tons, or trains containing 250 tons of merchandize. With assistance at the mountain, one such engine may therefore move a load of this weight through the line, in less than 22 hours; and engines starting from each end of the road each day, might pass each other in the centre, and convey 500 tons through the line, without interruption.

The annual tonnage passed over the work under such circumstances, would be 182,500 tons. If an engine started from each end of the road every 12 hours, there would be required three places of meeting, and their annual performance would be 365,000 tons carried through the whole line.

If two trains were started from each end every 12 hours, there need still be but three places of meeting, and their annual duty would be 730,000 tons carried over the whole line.

The aggregate tonnage (exclusive of lumber,) of all the canals of the state of New York, is more than 20 per cent. less than this amount.

Admitting that the trade is more lively at some seasons of the year than at others—that the trains are sometimes loaded in one direction, and empty in the other—and that many circumstances interfere with that regular distribution of the supply here supposed, we will still be compelled to admit, that the arrangement will be adequate for any probable trade that can be expected upon the line.

If we suppose that these, or other circumstances, should render the actual performance but one-third of that which it is here shown could be conveniently accomplished, we would still have the annual trade of 240,000 tons carried through the line. And this is probably more than will ever be obtained by any rail road between the Atlantic and the western waters.

I deem a single track, therefore, sufficient for this road, and have advised the rejection of the additional one.

II. ADVANTAGES OF DIMINISHED SPEED.

I will state, in a few words, the sources of the advantages which I hope to derive by diminishing the velocity of transportation, without attempting to fix any particular estimate on their value. These are,

I.   That a reduction of the velocity will reduce the wear and tear of the engines, and the charges for their repair. Their durability will, therefore, of course be increased:

II.   That the durability of the cars will be increased, and the tax for their repair and renewal likewise diminished:

III.   That the durability of the road will be greater, and the annual charges for its maintenance less :

IV.   That the useful effect of the engine will be greater, and the consumption of fuel less, in proportion to the useful labor performed :

V.   That the load carried by the engine, and the useful labor performed in a given time being greater, the number of engines and the number of agents engaged in the transportation department, will be reduced :

VI.   That the power of the engines being increased, and the repairs which they need being diminished, the number of engines, from this cause also, may be reduced.

VII.   The strains upon the cars being reduced, their strength, and consequently their weight, may be reduced ; a circumstance which will increase the proportion of goods to the weight of cars in the train, and of course, increase the effective performance :

VIII.   The strain upon the wheels and axles being less, for the same gross weight, the ratio of the diameter of the wheel to that of the axle, may be increased ; and consequently, the resistance at the axle will be diminished, and the load conveyed will be augmented :

IX.   The risk of accidents, and consequent damages, will be less.

III. ADVANTAGE OF HEAVY ENGINES.

The weight of engines in ordinary use at this time, is much greater than it was customary to adopt on their first successful application on the Liverpool and Manchester rail-way.

Their dimensions are still increasing, and are only limited, on lines where a heavy business is transacted, by the strength of the roads which they traverse.

I have proposed that the James river and Kanawha road be made with a view to still heavier engines. The principal advantages which will result from the arrangement, will be

I. That a smaller number of engines will be needed for the same duty; and the capital invested in them will accordingly be less:

II. That the number of engines being diminished, the cost of repairs will be reduced nearly in the same proportion:

III. That the number of agents required for the management of the engines will be reduced just in proportion to the reduction of the number of engines:

IV. That a saving will be effected in the aggregate cost, and expense of repairs, of the tenders:

V. That a considerable economy of fuel will result from the change.

OF THE WAREHOUSES.

The usual charges for transshipment and forwarding constitute a heavy burthen on the trade.

At the termini of many of the principal lines of the country, these charges are from 6 to $12\frac{1}{2}$ cents per 100 pounds.

A charge of 10 cents per 100 pounds, is equal to $2 24 per ton; and at this rate, a trade of 100,000 tons would be taxed $224,000 for this purpose. By the examinations in this volume, it has been shown, that the revenue of the line is diminished by a sum at least equal to the tax imposed on the trade. To pay a revenue of $224,000, would require an increase of trade on the James river and Kanawha improvement, of nearly 50,000 tons, to be carried through the whole line.

A tax of $2 24 on a ton, is equal to the charge for freight on 180 miles of canal; and for each cent that the cost of trans-shipment on 100 pounds is increasad, that weight might be transported through 18 miles of the canal. For each cent that this charge is increased, the trade of the space of 15 miles of the valley of the Ohio, or more than 3,000 tons of merchandize, would be excluded from the line.

The importance of the subject cannot, therefore, but be appreciated.

To obviate the necessity of this burthen on the trade, I have recommended that the warehouses at Covington, where the transshipment from the rail road to the canal has place, be erected by the company, and occupied by their agents; and that those on the Kanawha, where the the merchandise transshipped will be carried beyond the line of the improvement, be likewise erected by the company, and placed in the occupation of forwarding merchants, on such terms as are considered requisite for the protection of the trade.

The object of this arrangement is to put it in the power of the company to prevent a new tax from being levied on the tonnage, by a party which has less interest in its inerease than that possessed by the company. See Art. 60.

IMPROVEMENT OF THE KANAWHA.

87¾ MILES.

The Kanawha, from a point 6 miles below the Great Falls, to the Ohio, is to be improved so as to become navigable for steamboats of 100 tons burthen.

The examination made during the past summer, has furnished satisfactory evidence, that a minimum depth of 3½ feet of water can be obtained throughout, with the exception of points occurring at eight of the principal shoals. I have accordingly designated this as the proper depth to be sought, and recommended the enlargement and extension of the sluices for the purpose.

At the shoals, the plan contemplates the construction of short canals and locks for steamboats, in the river. These canals will be cut through the shoals, and the locks are designed to overcome the fall.

By the application of the method, the navigation will be rendered always sufficient for freighted boats of the medium class; and, excepting at the lowest stages of the water, for those of higher tonnage.

The shoals will be improved even where the locks are established, so that they may be ascended whenever the water is above its summer level.

ESTIMATE

Of the cost of Transporting one ton of Goods from Richmond to Point Pleasant.

ASSUMED FREIGHT 100,000 TONS.

The James River and Kanawha line is considered, in this estimate, to be composed of $238\frac{88}{100}$ miles of canal, with an area of cross section of 200 square feet ; $138\frac{3}{10}$ miles of rail road, with a single track, and $87\frac{75}{100}$ miles of steamboat navigation, with a minimum depth of water of $3\frac{1}{2}$ feet.

I. COST OF FREIGHT ON CANALS.

The report of the canal commissioners of New York, for 1837, states the cost of freight, exclusive of toll, on agricultural products, to be for the Erie canal, 9 mills per ton of 2,000 pounds per mile.

The report of the board of managers of the Lehigh Canal Company, for 1837, gives for the price of transporting coal on that work, $\frac{3}{4}$ cents per ton per mile.

The usual price of freight on the Schuylkill canal, is one dollar for transporting one ton of coal a distance of 108 miles ; a sum equivalent to $\frac{93}{100}$ of a cent per ton per mile.

I might name other facts, which would go to establish the same point, viz : that the customary price of freight on canals, in this country, is from three-fourths of a cent to one cent per ton of 2,000 lbs. per mile, for gross articles.

The James river and Kanawha canal being larger than

those which give this result, will justify the assumption, that similar articles will be carried on it for less. I shall, therefore, be authorised to assume, that the charge will certainly be not more than 9 mills per ton of 2,240 pounds per mile.

The current expenses for the repairs and agencies on the Erie and Champlain canals appear to have increased *pari passu*, and in the same ratio, with the increase of trade. For the year 1837, they amounted to $425,539\frac{39}{100}$.

The whole amount of tonnage cleared from these canals in the same year, was for the Erie canal, 647,511 tons, and for the Champlain canal, 321,837 tons.

Of these quantities, 72,090 tons went to or from Buffalo, and 59,381 tons to or from Whitehall, the northern extremity of the Champlain canal.

Now, it is not practicable to ascertain how far each ton was carried along the line; but if it be admitted, that all that was received at, or forwarded from, Buffalo and Whitehall, traversed the whole line, and that the balance was transported over half the lengths of the lines, we shall probably be near enough to the truth for the object in view.

We shall then have, on the Champlain canal, 59,381 tons carried 64 miles, or what is equivalent thereto, 3,800,384 tons carried one mile,

And 262,456 tons carried 32 miles, or   8,398,592 tons carried one mile.

And for the Erie canal,

72,090 tons carried 363 miles, or   26,168,670 tons carried one mile,

And 575,421 tons carried $181\frac{1}{2}$ miles, or 104,438,911 tons carried one mile.

The sum of these numbers amounts to 142,806,557 tons carried to the distance of one mile.

The total expenses for agencies and repairs, on these two works, amounted during this same period, to 425,539,390 mills; from which we obtain, by dividing by the number of tons, $2\frac{93}{100}$ mills per ton per mile, for the value of superintendence and repairs.

This, however, is for the ton of 2,000 pounds; and reduced to the ton of 2,240 pounds, will give $3\frac{34}{100}$ mills for the value of these expenses.

The expenses for repairs and agencies for the Schuylkill canal amounted, in 1826, to $102,718 06 cents.

The number of tons conveyed was 631,163.

It is not practicable to determine the exact distance this tonnage was transported on the work; but we shall be near the truth, if we consider it equivalent to 550,000 tons carried 100 miles, or 55,000,000 tons carried a distance of one mile.

If we divide the cost of repairs, in mills, by this number, we shall obtain $1\frac{87}{100}$ mills per ton per mile—the ton being that used on the public improvements of Pennsylvania.

Reduced to the ton of 2,240 pounds, there will result the charge of 2 mills per ton per mile, for these expenses.

The James and Kanawha canal is larger than the preceding; the injury to the banks will consequently be less serious, and it would probably be permissible to estimate these charges, in the application to that work, something lower.

But the trade assumed is much less; and preferring to be on the safe side, I deem it most prudent to estimate the item at a higher sum than either of those found above; and I shall accordingly assume, for the value of this charge, *three and a half mills per ton per mile.*

My estimate will consequently be, for freight on heavy produce, **9** mills; cost of repairs and superintendence, $3\frac{1}{2}$ mills. Total expense of transportation, exclusive of toll, $1\frac{1}{4}$ *cents per ton per mile.*

COST OF FREIGHT ON RAIL ROADS.

It will be convenient to divide the expense of freight into four classes, viz:

I. The cost of repairs for the road;

II. The cost of motive power;

III. The expense of agencies for the transportation;

IV. The maintenance of the cars.

I. I have estimated in my report of this year, the cost of repairs for a single track, with a trade of 100,000 tons, at **$1133** per mile; which is equivalent to $11\frac{33}{100}$ *mills per ton per mile.*

II. It is stated in the appendix to De Pambour's work on Locomotive Engines, that, after having for a long time kept and repaired their engines themselves, the directors of the Stockton and Darlington rail road entered into a contract, by which they agree "to pay $\frac{4}{10}$ of a penny per ton of *goods* carried to a distance of one mile; and, for that price, the contractors have undertaken not only to keep the engines in good repair, furnishing workmen and materials, but also to pay all the current expenses of haulage, such as salary of the engine-men, fuel, oil, grease, &c. Besides this, they must pay the company an interest of 5 per cent. on the capital representing the value of the engines, and of all the establishments placed at their disposal for working."

I know of no reason why the same duty cannot be done on the same terms, on the James River and Kanawha improvement,—where the grades are not less favorable, where the fuel will be exceedingly cheap, where the business in the two directions will be less unequally divided, and it is proposed that the speed will be less. I shall accordingly estimate the item at 8 *mills per ton per mile.**

III. For the transportation of this trade, there will be required with the trains, at the watering stations, and at the dépôts, a constant force,—over and above those employed in the repairs of the road, engines and cars, and in the collection of toll, and transshipment of produce,—of about

80 men at, $1 00 per diem, - - -	$80 00
2 superintendents, at $5 00 per diem, -	10 00
Daily expense of agencies for transportation,	$90 00

per diem, or $32,850 per annum.

This sum, divided by the number of tons, and the distance, will yield $2\frac{27}{100}$ *mills per ton per mile.*

IV. To transport 100,000 tons per annum, if we suppose the cars to contain an average load of three tons of goods,

* On the Columbia and Philadelphia rail road, the cost of this item is more than double the amount assumed in my estimate; but the road is bad, the curves abrupt, the grades steep, the velocity high, and the engines frequently start with partial loads.

there will be required **33,333** cars to pass over the line ; or, we may say, 90 cars per diem.

To keep this number of cars constantly in motion, on the work, there must be an equal number always at the dépôts.

But the quantity of trade will sometimes be less than half the average quantity, and sometimes more than double the average. Supposing it at any period to be double, there would be needed not less than 360 cars to transact the business of the line. But there will always be some in the shops, and some, for other reasons, not available. I estimate the whole number at five hundred.

Putting the average cost of such cars at $280, and supposing them to last 7 years, and to need an annual expenditure for their repair of $30, we shall have for the expense which will be incurred by the 500 cars,

Interest on cost of 500 cars at $280 each,	$8,400
Annual deterioration at $40 each, - -	20,000
Annual repairs at $30 each, - - -	15,000
Annual expense of cars, - - -	$43,400

Dividing by the length of the line in miles, and the number of tons, we shall obtain **3.14** *mills per ton per mile.*

The cost of freight on the road will then be,

For repairs of road, - - - -	11.33 mills
" motive power. &c. - - -	8.00 "
" salaries of agents, - - -	2.27 "
" maintenance of cars, - - -	3.14 "
Aggregate, - - - - -	2.474 cents.

In the examples throughout this volume, I have set down the cost of freight on the rail road, at 2½ *cents per ton per mile.*

COST OF FREIGHT ON THE KANAWHA RIVER.

I assume that the cost of freight on the Kanawha, when the improvements of its navigation shall have been completed, will not differ essentially from that on the Ohio river, when the height of the water will permit the ascent of large boats.

By this statement, I do not mean that goods would be taken from the termination of the rail road, and delivered at Point Pleasant, at the prices per ton per mile for which they are carried from Pittsburg to St. Louis; but that the charge on a steamboat ascending the Ohio with a load, will not be greater for carrying it 88 miles up the Kanawha, than for running the same distance up the Ohio.

The average freight from Pittsburg to Louisville, in good water, may be estimated at 25 cents per 100 lbs., and from Pittsburg to St. Louis, at 50 cents per 100 lbs. It is frequently much higher, and it is sometimes lower.

When it is lower, it is the consequence of competition, and when it is higher, it may be attributed either to a sudden increase of tonnage, or deficiency of boats, or to the unfavorable state of the river.

A fair average, in good water, is the prices named above— which is equivalent to about 9 mills per ton per mile.

The general price of freight from New Orleans to Cincinnati, may be considered to be about 50 cents per 100 lbs.; or three-fourths of a cent per ton per mile.

I am of opinion, that when the navigation of the Ohio is

improved, the charges upon it will be lower than the present
prices on the Mississippi; and I am confident, that the improvement of the Kanawha will permit nearly the same prices
to prevail on that river as on the Ohio.

I estimate, accordingly, the transportation on the Kanawha
at the assumed average for the present prices on the Mississippi, or ¾ *of a cent per ton per mile.*

It is not easy to anticipate the cost of maintenance, for the
improvements on this river. I think, however, that $250 per
mile will be ample for the purpose. If we make this assumption, we shall have for the

Transportation on the Kanawha, 7½ mills per ton per mile.
Maintenance of the works,   2½   "   "   "

Making the aggregate charge for *freight,* 1 *cent per ton per
mile.*

COST OF TRANSSHIPMENTS.

I have proposed, in my report, that the transshipments at
Covington shall be effected by the agents of the company.
But that although warehouses should be established there, and
occupied by the company, the principal part of the freight
ought to be lifted directly from the boats to the cars, and from
the cars to the boats. The cars should run along side of the
boats, directly under the crane, where every advantage of
power can be exerted. I think that six men can shift the lading of a 50 tons boat into the cars, in two hours. The average
daily transshipments will be about 300 tons; and supposing
the force to work twelve hours per diem, six men would be
sufficient to unload and re-load that quantity. But in business

of this nature, at least one half the time would be lost, and a force would consequently be required twice as great as would seem to be absolutely needed. And the trade will sometimes be twice as great as the average value, and we shall have, therefore, to estimate for a constant force of **24**, instead of **6** men.

There would be required two clerks, and two assistant clerks, and a general superintendent of transshipments.

My estimate will then stand,

24 men, at **$1** 00 per diem, - - -	**$24** 00
2 clerks, at 3 00 do. - - - -	6 00
2 assistant clerks, 1 50 do. - - - - -	3 00
1 superintendent, do. - - - -	6 00
Expenses at Covington, - - - -	**$39** 00

per diem, or $14,235 per annum.

To which add rent of warehouses $3,000.

Annual charges for transshipments, **17,235** dollars,—which is equivalent to 17¼ cents per ton.

The transshipment at the Kanawha will be higher, since storage will frequently be encountered, and it will not be so much in the control of the company. We shall, however, be able to render the accomplishment of the business very convenient, and I doubt not, that the charge on heavy articles may be reduced, when storage is not incurred, to 50 *cents per ton.*

SUMMARY STATEMENT.

Freight on $238\frac{88}{100}$ miles of canal, a $1\frac{1}{4}$ cents, $2 98½

    do. $138\frac{30}{100}$ do.   rail road a 2.47 do.   3 41½

    do. $87\frac{75}{100}$ do. steamboat navigation, a 1 cent, 87¾

Transshipment at Covington,   17¼

Charges at Loup Creek,   50

Freight from Richmond to Point Pleasant, $7 95

per ton; or, neglecting the fraction, I estimate the average charge for freight on the whole line, at $1\frac{7}{10}$ *cents per ton per mile.*

Of this tax, probably $13\frac{1}{2}$ mills would be independent of the amount of trade, and the residue would represent the portion due to the constant expenses, and would consequently be reciprocally as the tonnage.

If we assume, in pursuance of this estimate, that the cost of freight will be $1\frac{7}{10}$ cents per ton per mile, on the completion of the improvement, and that the average toll will be (Art. 191), 1 cent per ton per mile, we shall have $12 60, for the whole tax on every ton transported from Point Pleasant to Richmond. Of this sum, $7 95 will be consumed in the expense of carriage, and the balance, or $4 65 will be divided among the stockholders.

We have assumed for the Ohio trade, 100,000 tons; and the aggregate tax upon it will consequently be $1,260,000. Of this sum $795,000, will go to bear the actual cost and profit for conveyance, and the remaining $465,000 will be distributed as dividend.

Suppose now, we permit, at any point, the introduction of a

plan that will tax the trade but 5 cents per one hundred pounds
more than is anticipated in this estimate. The consequence
will be, (if we do not sacrifice a portion of the tonnage,) the
addition of $1 12, or about 14 per cent. to the cost of convey-
ance of every ton, or to increase the expenses of the line
$112,000, and diminish the profits an equal amount—making
the cost of freight $907,000, and reducing the profits on this
portion of the trade down to $353,000.

Nothing is more easy—as we will perceive, indeed, by a
glance at three-fourths of the improvements in the country—
than to consume all the tax that can be imposed on the trade,
in the expense of its transportation.

ESTIMATE.

The estimate of the cost of the work is, for

$238\frac{88}{100}$ miles of canal, - - - -	$6,500,000
$138\frac{30}{100}$ " " rail road, with cars, and en-gines, &c., - - - - - - ..	2,602,950
$87\frac{75}{100}$ miles of Kanawha river, - - -	408,098
Total, - - - - - -	$9,511,048

This sum is exclusive of damages, and the cost of connecting the line with tide-water, at Richmond. These expenses
included, will make the aggregate about $10,000,000.

TONNAGE OF THE OHIO AND MISSISSIPPI.

IMPORTS INTO NEW ORLEANS.

(*From Levy's New Orleans Price Current, for Oct. 1st,* 1838.)

The following are the principal imports into New Orleans from the interior, for the year ending the 30th of September, 1838.

Apples,	- - - -	bbls. - -	24,908
*Bacon, assorted,	- -	hhds. and casks,	11,328
" hams,	- - -	hhds. - -	5,275
" in bulk, -	- -	lbs. - -	984,490
Bagging, Kentucky,	- -	pieces, - -	42,331
Bale rope,	- - - -	coils, - -	52,897
Butter,	- - - -	kegs and firkins,	11,279
Beef, -	- - - -	barrels, - -	6,131
" dried, -	- - -	lbs. - -	44,050
*Cotton, Louisiana and Mississippi, bales,		- -	561,225
" Mobile,	- - - " -	- -	22,900
" Lake,	- - - " -	- -	13,892
" North Alabama and Tennessee, bales,		-	124,495
" Arkansas, Florida and Texas, bales,		-	20,706
Corn, in ears,	- - -	bbls. - -	269,354
" shelled,	- - -	sacks, - -	169,295
Coal, western,	- - -	bbls. - -	99,220
*Flour,	- - - -	bbls. - -	307,610
Lard,	- - - -	kegs, - -	219,080
Lead,	- - - -	pigs, - -	310,102
Oats, -	- - - -	bbls. - -	25,269
Potatoes,	- - - -	bbls. - -	12,956
*Pork,	- - - -	bbls. - -	138,583
" in bulk,	- - -	lbs. - -	3,474,076
*Tobacco, Leaf,	- - -	hhds. - -	37,706
" Chewing,	- -	kegs and boxes,	3,974
Whiskey, -	- - -	bbls. - -	50,011

* Of the FLOUR received at New Orleans, 163,686 bbls. were exported ;

PENNSYLVANIA CANAL.

The following abstract from the annual report of the collector, for the central improvement of the state of Pennsylvania, is copied from Harris' Intelligencer and Pittsburg Prices Current, for November 17, 1838.

Collector's Office, Alleghany, Nov. 1, 1838.

" Abstract from the annual report made from this office for the fiscal year, ending 31st. October, 1838.

Cleared eastward from this office,

Bbls. Flour,	- - - - -	**101,725**
Bush. Wheat,	- - - - -	**48,057**
" Corn and other grain,	- -	**1,713**
Bbls. Pork,	- - - - -	**1,007**
Lbs. Bacon,	- - - - -	**8,211,175**

and of this quantity, 75,528 bbls. were sent coast-wise, and 88,158 bbls. to Cuba and other foreign ports.

Of the PORK received, 89,271 bbls. were exported ; and of this quantity, 85,250 bbls. were shipped coast-wise, and but 4,021 bbls. to foreign ports.

Of the BACON received there 10,800 hhds. were exported; and of this quantity, 10,180 hhds. were sent coast-wise, and but 620 hhds. to foreign ports.

Of the TOBACCO received in New Orleans, 37,076 hhds. were exported ; and of this quantity, 15,503 hhds. were sent coast-wise—10,072 hhds. of which were shipped to New York, and 1652 hhds. to Philadelphia.

Of the COTTON received in New Orleans, about *one seventh* of the whole quantity, or 105,749 bales were sent coast-wise ;—and of this portion, 39,352 bales were shipped to New York, and 40,271 bales to Boston.

Lbs. Feathers,	-	-	-	-	-	35,682
" Wool,	-	-	-	-	-	865,677
" Cotton,	-	-	-	-	-	1,045,350
" Hemp,	-	-	-	-	-	908,232
" Tobacco,	-	-	-	-	-	4,880,915
" Furs and Peltry,		-	-	-		159,656
Gallons of Liquor,	-	-	-	-		25,291
Lbs. Merchandise,	-	-	-	-		690,702
" Groceries,	-	-	-	-		315,680
" Furniture,	-	-	'	-		330,221
Boxes Window Glass,	-	-	-			4,532
Lbs. Rags,	-	-	-	-		41,492
Tons Mineral Coal,	-	-	-			265
Lbs. Pigs and Castings,	..	-	-			409,418
Lbs. Blooms Iron and Nails,	-	-	-			1,880,357
Number of Boats cleared,	-	-	.			2,505
Miles travelled by Passengers,	.ı	-				3,050,170
Total amount of Tonnage,		-				48,210,282*lbs.*

ARRIVED FROM THE EASTWARD.

Bbls. Fish,	-	-	-	-	-	7,294
Lbs. Butter and Cheese,		-	-	-		111,325
" Queensware,		-	-	-		2,225,320
" Hardware,		-	-	..	-	4,449,080
Bush. of Salt,	-	-	-	-	-	140,935
" Potatoes,		-	-	-	-	3,789
Lbs. of Hemp,		-	-	-	-	392,632
" Tobacco,	.	-	`	.		66,669
" Leather,		-	-	-	-	212,420

Galls. of Liquor,	70,023
" Oil,	76,381
Lbs. Merchandise,	12,672,641
" Groceries,	7,456,634
" Drugs and Dyestuffs,	230,244
Tons of Gypsum, -	22
Lbs. Furniture,	1,691,137
Tons Mineral Coal,	1,001
Lbs. Pigs and Castings,	1,193,302
" Blooms and bar Iron,	15,172,607
" Copper and Tin,	423,192
" Marble and Bar Blocks,	1,385,508
Cords of Wood,	651
" Bark,	353
Tons of Hay,	90
Total amount of Tonnage, -	64,884,461*lbs.*

The above statement of items embraces only the most prominent articles—a number of minor items being left out; but the totals of Tonnage both East and West are correct."

We will perceive, from this statement, and those relating to the imports into New Orleans, that the quantity of FLOUR shipped from the latter city to the northern ports, was but 25 per cent. less than the whole quantity sent from Pittsburg eastward, by the Pennsylvania improvement. And that the quantity so shipped was subjected to a charge of 10 cents per barrel, for receiving and forwarding in New Orleans, and 60 cents per barrel for freight, besides the charges actually incurred in New Orleans; and, if detained there, the additional charge for storage.

It appears, also, that more than four times the whole quantity of TOBACCO carried through the line, was shipped from New Orleans to the northern ports—being subject to a charge of $4 00 for freight, $1 00 for receiving and forwarding, 50 cents per month for storage, expenses actually incurred, &c.

It also appears that twice as much BACON was sent coastwise, as passed over that improvement; and was charged nearly as much per hhd. as the tobacco.

All these stores are liable to the risk of injury, in the climate of New Orleans, for which no specific value can be named.

BUSINESS OF THE OHIO CANAL.

The following slip contains, probably, authentic information relative to the most important business of the Ohio canal—from April 12th, to Nov. 18th, 1838.

" The canal opened at Cleaveland, on the 12th of April, from which time to the first of November, instant, there were received at the port of Cleaveland, via the Ohio canal:

Bush. of Wheat,	1,122,732
Bbls. of Flour,	252,680
" of Pork,	30,816
Lbs. of Butter,	451,890
Bush. of Corn,	102,224
Bbls. of Whiskey,	8,894
Lbs. of Bacon,	1,535,631
" of Lard,	979,556
Hhds. of Bacon,	301

And during the same time, there cleared that port, via the canal:

Bbls. of Salt,	-	-	-	-	..	53,968
Lbs. of Gypsum,	-	-	-	-	-	1,378,287
Bbls. of Lake Fish,	-	-	-	-		6,967
Lbs. of Merchandise,	-	-	-	-		13,383,980

This statement shows the importance of the Pennsylvania or Ohio canal, or Cross Cut. Had that work been completed, a very large amount of the above produce and merchandise would have been carried through Pennsylvania. But we feel bound also, to say, that in our opinion the Pennsylvania and Ohio canal will never be complete, or of any great utility, until the main line of the Pennsylvania canal is extended from Pittsburg to Beaver."—*Bicknell's Reporter*.

It would appear from this abstract, that there were carried northward to Lake Erie, by the Ohio canal, during the year, more than twice as much flour as was shipped from Pittsburg for the east by the Pennsylvania improvement.

There was also carried southwardly—probably for the valley of the Ohio and Mississippi—rather more merchandise than was sent westwardly from Philadelphia.

It does not follow, however, that this trade would have been brought to Pennsylvania, by the "Cross Cut" canal, if the latter had been finished. To produce this result, the charges on the Pennsylvania improvement must be first reduced.

From the best data I can obtain, I estimate the

Imports into New Orleans, from the interior, at	**300,000**	tons.
Exports up the Mississippi, at ¼ the imports, or	**75,000**	"
Trade of the Pennsylvania line, .. -	**60,000**	"
Tonnage sent from the Ohio to New York, and from New York to the Ohio, -	**20,000**	"
Tonnage from Baltimore to Wheeling, and from Wheeling to Baltimore, - -	**15,000**	"
Making in all, - - - - -	**470,000**	tons;

but without including the trade which is imported and exported directly from the cities on the Mississippi, above New Orleans, which would probably make for the true aggregate, more than 500,000.

NEW ORLEANS TARIFF OF CHARGES.

GENERAL TARIFF OF COMMISSIONS, EXCLUSIVE OF CHARGES ACTUALLY INCURRED.

On sales of Sugar, Molasses, Cotton, Tobacco and Lead, - - - - - -	2½ per cent.
All other produce or merchandise, - - -	5 "
Guarantee of do. if not exceeding 6 months, -	2½ "
And for each month additional over 6 months, -	½ "
Purchase and shipment of merchandise and produce, - - - - - - -	2½ "

RATES FOR RECEIVING AND FORWARDING GOODS.

(Exclusive of charges actually incurred.)

Sugar,	-	-	-	per hhd.	- - - $1 00
Tobacco,	-	-	-	" "	- - - 1 00
"	-	-	-	" keg or box,	- - 20
Cotton,	-	-	-	" bale,	- - - 1 00
Liquids,	-	-	-	" pipe,	- - - 1 00
Flour,	-	-	-	" bbl.	- . - 10
Lard,	-	-	-	" keg,	- - - 5
Iron,	-	-	-	" 2,000 lbs.	- - 1 00

RATES OF STORAGE.

					Per month.
Cotton,	-	-	-	per bale,	- - $ 20
Tobacco,	-	-	-	" hhd.	- - 50
Bacon,	-	-	-	" hhd.	- - 25
Pork and Whiskey,	-			" bbl.	- - 10
Flour,	-	-	-	" bbl.	- - 6
Lard,	-	-	-	" keg,	- - 5
Sugar,	-	-	-	" hhd.	- - 37½

FREIGHT.

(For October 1st. 1838.)

Cotton to Liverpool,	-	per lb.	-	-	½d.
" " Havre,	- -	"	-	-	1⅛cts.
" " New York,	-	"	-	-	½ct.
Tobacco to London,	-	"	-	-	48s.
" " New York,	-	per hhd.	-	-	$4 00
Bacon " North of Hatteras,	"	-	-	$3 00
Flour, " Northern Ports,	"	-	-	60
Lead, " "	per ton,	-	-	2 50

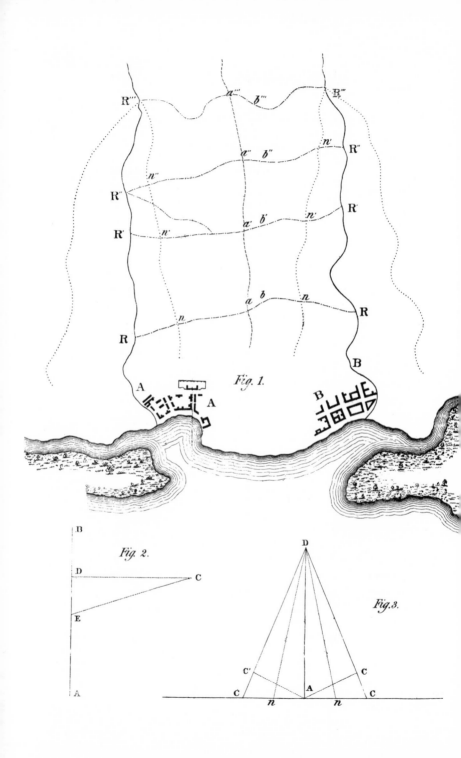

Fig. 1.

Fig. 2.

Fig. 3.

CONTENTS.

PART I.

§ I.

§ II.

§ III.

§ IV.

§ V.

§ VI.

§ VII.

§ VIII.

PART II.

TRADE OF THE OHIO AND MISSISSIPPI.

§ I.

§ IV.

§ V.

PART III.

PRACTICAL APPLICATIONS.

§ I.

§ II.

§ III.

§ IV.

§ v.

§ vi.

§ vii.

APPENDIX.